When the Bible Meets the Sky

The Star of Bethlehem and Other Mysteries

Frederick W. Baltz

ISBN: 9798479836039

DEDICATION

This book is dedicated to all the Wise Men and Women who look to the Scriptures as the Magi once looked to the Star .

CONTENTS

ACKNOWLEDGMENTS

My thanks to Cindy, my children, and the many friends who have encouraged me in my teaching, preaching, investigating, and writing. Thanks to Nancy Klauer and Pamela McKinsey for proofreading and editing the manuscript. Thanks to Elliot Baltz for designing the cover. Thanks to John P. Nielsen for background concerning the theoretical concept of the universal king in Mesopotamia. Thanks to Timothy Mahoney at Patterns of Evidence for his efforts in bringing some of the insights in this book to a wider audience.

Chapter 1: The Sky and What it Can Tell Us

Part of the college experience for many people is the forming of new friendships with students you meet, some who are like you, and others who are different. On my future wife Cindy's dormitory floor lived a young student named Sandy who grew up in Chicago. They were all invited to a mutual friend's wedding, and Cindy's parents' farm was on the way. Sandy was going to get to see a farm for the first time. From the campus they drove on highways, then blacktop roads, then gravel roads. The farm was four miles from a small town. So in the darkness of night, away from almost any artificial light, Sandy saw the night sky for the first time in her life. She had never known the experience of seeing all the stars. In the city the light pollution from thousands of street lights, along with the smoke from manufacturing, obscured the heavens every single night. The moon had been visible, and some bright stars and planets, but nothing like this. That experience is remembered to this day.

When *We* Look Up

When we look into the unobscured night sky we see some 4000 stars that could be counted if you had some way to keep track of them. The Milky Way runs as a crystal cloud or river from north to the south. Some objects appear bluish white; others appear red. Some really seem to be hanging lower than others, like stationary passenger jets ready to land.

You try to remember what you learned about the sky when you were in school. You look, and there it is, the Big Dipper. And what was that about two of the stars in the Dipper being in line as pointers? You look again, and there is the North Star; two stars in the Dipper did point to it. It's coming back to you. There is Orion's belt. Three bright stars close together in a row. The other three near it are the sword hanging from the belt. Maybe if you look long enough you will see a falling star. If you are in the right latitudes you might also see the Northern Lights. That will be unforgettable! If you can look to the sky and recognize most of this, you are about average for a 21st Century sky observer.

But any of us in the 21st Century who look up at the stars realize we are looking at massive objects so far away that we cannot begin to conceptualize the distance. The number of stars is so colossal that we cannot conceptualize that, either, nor even the numbers of galaxies which the individual stars make up. The age of this sky we are looking at is said to be twelve or fifteen billion years old. How it all began is a mystery. We are told that a "big bang" brought all matter and energy into being in an instant, concentrated at one dense point. It rushed outward to create and occupy the field of space. The subsequent evolution of that matter and energy happened within limits of incomprehensibly small tolerances, "fine tuning", as it is called.

Although there are many instances of fine tuning, we will cite just a few examples here, the "constants". Scientists speak of constants; there are five of them. Stop and think for a moment that there *are* constants, rather than perpetual irregularities in what see in the universe. Why is that so? (In fact, why should there be anything at all, rather than nothing at all?)

- First is the *gravitational force constant.* If gravity had been an unimaginably small amount weaker, no stars could have formed, and no life could exist. If it had been an incomprehensibly small amount stronger, the stars would burn too quickly.
- The *electromagnetic constant* determines what happens within atoms and molecules. The slightest change in this constant would mean particles could not bond. Result: no life—no anything.
- The *strong nuclear force* is what holds atomic nuclei together. It is a constant, and because it is a constant of precisely the right strength, atoms can happen.
- The *weak nuclear force* constant is another recognized and measured force that controls radioactive decay. The slightest change in the strength of this constant would have led to a dead end as far as life is concerned in the universe.
- The *cosmological constant* controls the speed at which the universe expands. If the change in that speed were different by a value as small as *1 part in* 10^{120} the universe would have either flown apart or collapsed upon itself.

So when we look up, many of us see evidence for a Creator if we know what to look for, and where and when to look for it. Even if we have no such knowledge, many look at the sky and simply say: there must be a Creator.

When we look up we are aware that what we call "outer space" begins past what we call the "atmosphere". That's the air we breathe, a mixture of gasses. Within the atmosphere are the clouds, the lightning, the thunder, the wind and the rain. They all follow laws, so to some extent, weather can be predicted. Beyond the atmosphere is where only rockets can travel, because they carry their own oxygen. What we call the sky is a part of the universe showing through the clear atmosphere to us. When we look up at night, we see awesome beauty. But we have some idea of just what we are looking at. We learned it in school.

When *They* Looked Up

People in ancient times were much more sky-aware than people now. They knew nothing about it in terms of the science that children today are taught in school. But they didn't have the myriad distractions we do. No TV, no movies, no night-time homework or football games. People spent more time in darkness. There was the sky, available to them all every night. They looked up more than we do.

People told stories about what was up there, stories that had been heard for ages. The lore about the sky grew as the generations passed. People had their ideas of what the sky was made of, and how its constituent parts operated. The sun, for example, rode a chariot across the sky daily.

From the earliest times some of those ancient people became observers and recorders of what they saw as the sky went through its annual changes. Later observers were able to build on that knowledge. In Egypt priests noticed that each day a new part of the sky would appear on the eastern horizon before the sun rose. The reappearance of the Dog Star, Sirius, became the sign for the beginning of each new year. Sumerians, Assyrians, and Babylonians all advanced their knowledge of the sky through record keeping and study. All ancient sky observers divided the revolving sky into sections, often twelve of them. This was the zodiac. They found other marker stars to subdivide the sky. These were the decans. Some civilizations used 24, others used 36.

Those observers of the sky envisioned something quite different from what we do. To us the stars are giant balls of gas burning with nuclear fire. To the ancient people, all the clouds, the winds and weather, the sun and moon, comets and meteors, besides the stars and planets made up one sky, one heaven. This heaven might be subdivided into ascending crystal spheres, but it was still a unity of all things above the earth, up there and mysterious. This was the place, people reasoned, where lived the real "influencers" of the world.

> *To me, though I am the very least of all the saints, this grace was given, to preach to the Gentiles the unsearchable riches of Christ, and to bring to light for everyone what is the plan of the mystery hidden for ages in God, who created all things,* ***so that through the church the manifold wisdom of God might now be made known to the rulers and authorities in the heavenly places.*** Ephesians 3:8-10

In the Book of Enoch, a writing which is not part of the Bible, though it is quoted in the Bible (Jude 14-15), we find a section called the Book of the Heavenly Luminaries. In the book, Enoch who lived at the time shortly after the creation of the world, is shown a vision of the heavens. That is already of interest to us, because we will see this same idea with respect to Ezekiel and John the Elder who wrote the Revelation. In the vision the angel Uriel shows Enoch the secrets of the heavens and their workings. We learn that Jews in a time shortly before the New Testament thought of the sun as rising and setting in gates on the eastern and western horizons respectively. There were six gates to the East and six to the West. At each gate were many windows. These were the places where the sun and moon rose and set over the course of the year, moving along the horizon to the North and South as the seasons changed. This and much more is revealed by Uriel in Enoch so that faithful people might have understanding, and the holy days for the people of God would be observed when they were supposed to be, rather than at the wrong time.

Uriel tells Enoch:

> *"And the whole order of the stars shall be concealed from the sinners, and the thoughts on earth shall err concerning them, (and they shall be altered from all their ways), Yea, and they shall err and take them to be gods. And evil shall be multiplied upon them and punishment shall come upon them So as to destroy all."* 80, 7-8, R. H. Charles translation

This is what at least some very sincere Jews believed when they looked up in the years before Jesus was born. They saw a *raqia*, a firmament with stars in it, or on it. They believed waters were above that firmament, and maybe those waters were frozen and therefore clear. This was God's creation, and it had its own secrets which only the wisest people, like Solomon, knew.

Astrology?

An earlier Enoch passage (VIII, 1-4) tells the story of how the world descended into corruption and wickedness. First Azazel taught men to make swords, knives, shields, breastplates, with the knowledge of the metals necessary for these weapons. Further knowledge of ornaments and cosmetics led to fornication. "Baraq'al, (taught) astrology, Kokabel the signs, and Temel taught astrology, and Astradel the course of the moon." Clearly, to the Jews who read and used Enoch, astrology was an evil with a long history.

It is important to understand as we go forward that the Bible does not call upon us to embrace the pseudoscience of astrology. In the distant past all observation of the heavens was done from the earth with the hope of learning whatever might be learned. This was early scientific inquiry, and hypotheses were stated, then tested. For example, if a certain sign in the sky came before a drought on more than one occasion, someone might draw the conclusion that this sign should be regarded as an omen of drought in the future. But other omens were happening as well, simultaneously, and the whole system became complicated, cumbersome, and subjective. A look at the ancient works by Firmicus Maternus or Claudius Ptolemy demonstrate this well.

Astrologers persisted in the belief that theirs was truly a science which could benefit humans, whether kings or commoners. Some of them truly believed that. Many of the Jews disagreed. The Bible says God is the ruler of all. Astrology says stars, or gods they represent, or cosmic influences represented by the stars are in control. Some of the rabbis in Israel's history said that other nations might be ruled by the powers of the heavens, but those rules did not apply to God's people, because God is in charge of Israel. However, a small amount of astrological literature has been found among the Dead Sea Scrolls from Qumran (4Q186). Josephus wrote that the true founder of astrology was Abraham (*Antiquities* 1:154-168). Not all Jews rejected astrology.

But if astrology was generally considered bad, the actual worship of the hosts of heaven was absolutely forbidden. This was idolatry, the actual worship of other gods. In the history of the people of God are times when Israel committed this dreadful sin. An early warning against worshiping what is in the sky comes from Moses himself in Deuteronomy:

> *And beware lest you raise your eyes to heaven, and when you see the sun and the moon and the stars, all*

the host of heaven, you be drawn away and bow down to them and serve them, things that the LORD your God has allotted to all the peoples under the whole heaven. [20] *But the LORD has taken you and brought you out of the iron furnace, out of Egypt, to be a people of his own inheritance, as you are this day.* Deuteronomy 4:19-20

Upon their return from exile in Babylon the people of God had learned this lesson. They read Genesis, finding now the proper purpose of the lights in the sky:

[14] *And God said, "Let there be lights in the expanse of the heavens to separate the day from the night.* ***And let them be for signs and for seasons****, and* ***for days and years****,* [15] *and let them be lights in the expanse of the heavens* ***to give light upon the earth.*** *" And it was so.* [16] *And God made the two great lights—the greater light to rule the day and the lesser light to rule the night—and the stars.* [17] *And God set them in the expanse of the heavens to give light on the earth,* [18] *to rule over the day and over the night, and to separate the light from the darkness. And God saw that it was good.* [19] *And there was evening and there was morning, the fourth day.* Genesis 1:14-19

Fusing the Astral Horizons

H. G. Gadamer was a Christian philosopher who gave us the term: fusion of horizons. We all have our particular life situations or backgrounds that emerge as we live our lives. Each situation involves culture, experience, learning, beliefs, physical and mental abilities, and more. "Horizon" is the expression for the outer boundary of an individual's experience—everything in the person's situation. When we attempt to understand someone else by stepping inside that person's situation, we attempt to fuse horizons. We attempt to look beyond the farthest extent of our own background in order to see the world as another sees it.

Can we possibly fuse our 21st Century sky horizons with the sky horizons of ancient people and find something of value in the process? Can we successfully and profitably bring together the thinking of the distant past and of the present day? Can we from our perspective find meaning and truth as we step into their perspective? We have knowledge they never dreamed of. But did they also understand things some of us don't, or won't? People of faith should be open to this as a possibility.

But when *we* look up, we don't all see the same thing. Actually, we do, but we don't agree on what it is. Some of us are believers in God, and some are not. When we look up, some of us see the work of the Creator. Others choose not to. To those latter, we are an accident of the universe. We were bound to happen through random atomic and molecular interactions over time. It is hubris, they say, for us to think we are the only living, self-aware beings in the universe. Nothing is really special beyond any specialness we give it. There is no ultimate purpose or goal to anything. There are no absolute laws of good and evil—that is all relative. We decide those things, and we alone. That's what they say when they are honest.

The concept of the godless universe requires humanity to be altogether insignificant. Oh, from here on earth now, we may seem important. But we inhabit the Pale Blue Dot. On Valentine's Day in 1990 the Voyager 1 spacecraft recorded an image of earth from 3.8 billion miles away, 34 minutes before Voyager 1 was powered down forever on its way through our solar system into the infinite space beyond. In 1994 astronomer Carl Sagan, a spokesman for the godless universe viewpoint, had this to say about the image known as the Pale Blue Dot:

> "Our posturings, our imagined self-importance, the delusion that we have some privileged position in the Universe, are challenged by this point of pale light. Our planet is a lonely speck in the great enveloping cosmic dark. In our obscurity, in all this vastness, there is no hint that help will come from elsewhere to save us from ourselves."

Carl Sagan, Pale Blue Dot, © 1994 Carl Sagan, © 2000 Democritus Properties, LLC.

Figure 1. The Pale Blue Dot. This image of the Earth was secured by Voyager 1 in 1990. NASA.

That sounds cold, as cold as space. Atheists accept it. Believers don't.

The cosmology found in the Bible is not what the Scriptures are revealing when the Bible meets the sky. It is a cosmology shared by the ancient people of the Middle East. According to that cosmology, the earth was held up by pillars (but see Job 26:7, "He stretches out the north over the void and hangs the earth on nothing.".), the sky was a dome, waters were both beneath the dome and above it. Sheol, the abode of the dead, was beneath the earth. This is the language spoken by the people of the past. This is the world as they imagined it. The Bible uses those ideas without making them the content of its message.

The Bible is really about answering questions like: Why are we here? Is there really a God? What is right and what is wrong? Does it matter? Do I have an obligation to my neighbor? Do I have a purpose in life? Am I known by God; am I loved by God; will I live on because of God? Looking carefully into the science of the sky has summoned some people like astronomer Allan Sandage to a faith that once was absent from their lives. These people could see past the ancient cosmology embedded in the Scriptures to the truth conveyed by the Scriptures. When the Bible says: "In the beginning God created the heavens and the earth", it is not necessary to imagine the heavens and the earth as one would who lived three millennia ago. That sentence from Genesis still speaks profoundly to us as it tells us: *God created…* Scientists trace an amazing succession of events between the big bang and the present moment. Scientists can tell us something about how the creation came to be what it is, but in their role as scientists they cannot explain why. It's the theologian who says the truth has been revealed: *God created.*

The Bible meets the sky in more places than we will investigate within this book. There is more to be said. But when people of the Bible looked to the sky, they found instances of God acting and revealing himself to them. Believers in ancient times found their answers to meaning, purpose, relationship, and they believed God used the sky at times to reveal his Word to them. The sky is one means through which God has brought revelation, warning, hope, and promise.

When a most unusual star rose in the eastern sky, it was interpreted to mean that a King of the Jews had been born into the world. He would be the savior and the redeemer of the world. He would give eternal life. He came to us in our sinful world, and died for us, because we have an importance to him that is beyond comprehension. The Star of Bethlehem contradicts the godless, cold pointlessness of the atheists' Pale Blue Dot.

Supernatural and Natural

People draw a distinction between what is natural and what is supernatural. If God created all that is natural, and if God should choose to use the natural to communicate with us, that is already a kind of miracle. I believe many miracles are of this type. There may be explanations for these works of God, like the shadow moving backward. These explanations only apply to the "how" of what God has done. They are by no means an explaining-away of "what" God has done. Neither are they a denial that God has done them, rather than chance. As you will see, the intricate balance, the timing, the arranging of these miracles make them even more miraculous, not less. And why are they found in the history of God's people, but not in others?

We will now begin our investigation of some particular intersections of the Bible and the sky. From our perspective as people looking up in the 21st Century we have tools available that were not available in the past. These investigations will show that things considered unhistorical by some really happened. But that's not all. There is much more.

The Heavens Declare: A Test Case

The heavens declare the glory of God,
and the sky above proclaims his handiwork.
Psalm 19:1

The believer says: Amen! The heavens do declare the glory of God. And we are about to see that the heavens declare other things as well. The heavens bring affirmations of the biblical text, and they declare profound messages of faith. They declare truth sometimes spoken in the language of mathematics and astronomy. That particular kind of truth is enough to prove that the biblical Exodus really took place, and that it happened in 1446 B.C. We will investigate that now, and in the process we will discover further truth that affirms our belief in the integrity of the Bible.

As we apply some of the undeniable facts established by astronomers to the study of the Bible, we sometimes discover evidence pointing toward a supernatural use of natural phenomena which affirms the biblical text. The denial of a King David as the Bible presents him, the denial of the Exodus as the Bible describes it, and the denial of a conquest of Canaan as the Bible portrays it all meet insurmountable difficulties with the application of retro-calculated discoveries from the sky. For decades, some who are considered experts in academia, in archaeology, and in history have maintained that the biblical stories about the Exodus from Egypt, the conquest under Joshua, and the early monarchy under David in the Old Testament's golden age are not factual. The evidence, they say, does not support biblical claims, but actually contradicts it.

The Exodus is denied because of an claimed lack of written or physical evidence. No Egyptian source tells the same story of plagues, an Exodus, and then deliverance from Pharaoh's army as we find in the Scriptures. At least, that is what some claim.

The conquest of Canaan has been denied because the archaeological record from Canaan's settlements in the Twelfth and Eleventh Centuries doesn't support the presence of Israelites.

As for David, it has been argued that no evidence exists for a centralized, powerful monarchy at the time David is supposed to have lived. David, as the claim goes, was at the most a tribal figure whose story was greatly embellished. Why? So the nation of Israel would have an appropriate history, a past to be proud of.

Now we can demonstrate the failures of these assertions against the historical trustworthiness of the Bible with the evidence from the sky. We can even add precision to the biblical events which is not present in the biblical text itself.

- We can actually prove beyond any reasonable doubt that the Exodus occurred (see *Exodus Found*, pp. 129-132). We can state the year it happened, and the month, and the probable day. The importance of this must not be overlooked or ignored. Until now discussions of the Exodus have found both sides agreeing that there was no actual, final proof. With the discoveries in the sky and their application to the biblical texts, that is no longer true. We have proof of the Exodus, as we will demonstrate. It is a mathematical, statistical kind of proof that involves astronomy.
- We can find the sky event which was probably the mechanism for the miracle of the stopping sun when Joshua fought the Canaanites (Joshua 10). The Book of Joshua reports this event to have happened early in the conquest. A

sky event which was a solar eclipse happened at exactly the time indicated by the text. Tangentially, this evidence also affirms the account of the fall of Jericho; these stories are not baseless legends. This runs counter to the opinion that the conquest as presented in Joshua is far more exaggerated than factual. It has been said that Joshua's story of the fall of Jericho is at best the recollection of a minor battle long after the actual city was destroyed many years before Joshua and Israel even arrived there.

- In the application of the data that will confirm the integrity of the biblical stories we will also encounter an event from the last days of David. What we find in astronomical history will mesh completely with the portrayal of David, just as the Bible puts it forward in 2 Chronicles.

Two main theories concerning the time of the Exodus continue to be in competition. (These are set forward by those who do accept the reality of an Exodus, not those who deny it altogether.) The majority has placed the Exodus in the mid-Thirteenth Century B.C. This was the time of the great Pharaoh Ramses II. It was also just after the time that the archaeological data places the building of the store city of Ramses in Egypt. That is consistent with Exodus 1:11. But there is no evidence of Semitic slaves, nor of a killing of male babies belonging to those slaves. There is no evidence of Israelite names among the Egyptians at this time, either.

When we look to the earlier time proposed for the Exodus in the mid-Fifteenth Century B.C., we find all these. This is in fact the time that the Bible's own time references seem to require. *If 1 Kings 6:1 is taken at face value, we have an Exodus 480 years before the construction of Solomon's Temple.* That puts the Exodus in the Fifteenth Century.

In the four hundred and eightieth year after the people of Israel came out of the land of Egypt, in the fourth year of Solomon's reign over Israel, in the month of Ziv, which is the second month, he began to build the house of the LORD. 1 Kings 6:1

Others take 1 Kings 6:1 as a kind of symbolic approximation. That allows them to stay with the mid-Thirteenth Century Exodus theory. But there is another biblical statement that demands a time for the Exodus earlier than that of Ramses II. In Judges 11 the king of the Ammonites has demanded that Israel restore the villages in Heshbon and Aroer to the Ammonites. Jephthah the Judge responds that Israel had already lived there 300 years with no challenge from the Ammonites during that time. The time frame for Jephthah's words has to be at least 300 years later than the Exodus, and probably more. If the Exodus occurred in the mid-Thirteenth Century, that would place Jephthah three centuries later in 950. This is no longer in the period of the Judges, but in that of the monarchy that followed. But if the Exodus occurred in the mid-Fifteenth Century, this places Jephthah around 1150. That falls within the period of the Judges.

Returning now to the 1 Kings 6:1 time reference, we must understand that the accepted year among historians for the beginning of Solomon's reign is 971/970. His fourth year is therefore 967/966 B.C. 480 years before that year is 1446 B.C. (See J. Finegan, *Handbook of Biblical Chronology, Revised Edition.* Hendrickson, 1998. p. 201).

The time has come to look to the sky. NASA's eclipse lists provide the eclipse of the sun that was visible over Israel on July 14, 1406 B.C. (https://eclipse.gsfc.nasa.gov/SEcat5/catalog.html, eclipse number 01415). Solar eclipses are a rare sight anywhere on earth. Eclipses that approach totality are still rarer. What is so remarkable about this is its possible relationship to the event discussed in Joshua 10.

> *[12] At that time Joshua spoke to the LORD in the day when the LORD gave the Amorites over to the sons of Israel, and he said in the sight of Israel,*
> *"Sun, stand still at Gibeon,*
> *and moon, in the Valley of Aijalon."*
> *[13] And the sun stood still, and the moon stopped,*
> *until the nation took vengeance on their enemies.*

The book of Joshua places this stopping sun event at the beginning of the conquest of Canaan, after the fall of Jericho, and then the fall of Ai. According to the text, both these cities fell to Israel in a remarkably short time. Therefore, the stopping sun incident should have happened just forty years after the Exodus, because Israel wandered exactly forty years between the Exodus and start of the conquest. If the Exodus in fact happened in 1446 B.C., the eclipse of July 14, 1406 B.C., was in the correct year, in the correct time of year, and at the correct time of day to answer to the description of what happened for Joshua.

Stopping can mean to cease shining, or to cease moving. The latter is probably what is meant in the text. But the text implies there were storm clouds from which came hail stones. An eclipse of the sun behind clouds would be experienced as the sun returning to the sky from the place it was starting to set. In other words, it seemed to have stopped going down. For this July 14 eclipse to have happened in the same year the Bible places the stopping sun means this can hardly be a coincidence, especially given the rarity of eclipses in the first place.

This constitutes the proof of the Exodus. We are dealing with two separate streams of claimed historical tradition. 1 Kings 6:1, when understood against the chronology of the kings of Israel and Judah, places the Exodus in 1446 B.C. The sun stopping for Joshua, when understood in connection with the eclipse of 1406, places the Exodus forty years earlier in 1446 B.C. ***It is unthinkable that any tradition would carefully count history from an event that did not actually happen, let alone two traditions counting from that same***

event which did not actually happen. This is proof beyond any reasonable doubt that the Exodus occurred, and that it happened in 1446.

Centuries later, shortly before his death, King David took a census of the men in Israel capable of fighting in his army. 1 Chronicles 21:1 says it was inspired by Satan; 2 Samuel 24:1 says it was initiated by the Lord. This seeming discrepancy is part of a set of problems connected with the census. There is no question that it was understood as an evil thing which David should never have done. He ordered the census against the advice of his commander, Joab. Punishment came upon Israel because of it in the form of disease. So why did the Lord punish the nation for David's sin? What was so wrong about that census?

The answers to these questions involve specific directions for counting Israel found in Exodus.

> *[11] The LORD said to Moses, [12] "When you take the census of the people of Israel, then each shall give a ransom for his life to the LORD when you number them,* ***that there be no plague among them when you number them.*** *[13] Each one who is numbered in the census shall give this: half a shekel according to the shekel of the sanctuary (the shekel is twenty gerahs) half a shekel as an offering to the LORD. [14] Everyone who is numbered in the census, from twenty years old and upward, shall give the LORD's offering. [15] The rich shall not give more, and the poor shall not give less, than the half shekel, when you give the LORD's offering to make atonement for your lives. [16] You shall take the atonement money from the people of Israel and shall give it for the service of the tent of meeting, that it may bring the people of Israel to remembrance before the LORD, so as to make atonement for your lives."* Exodus 30:11-16

Counting the people was counting the Lord's people, not David's. Further, when a census was taken, each man was obligated to contribute ten gerahs as an offering to the Lord. There is no such requirement associated with David's census. It appears that David violated the Law, and possibly for the purpose of building the army, though the Lord had not called for it. David was guilty of a very serious transgression of the holy. Israel was complicit.

> [14] *So the LORD sent a pestilence on Israel, and 70,000 men of Israel fell.* [15] *And God sent the angel to Jerusalem to destroy it, but as he was about to destroy it, the LORD saw, and he relented from the calamity. And he said to the angel who was working destruction, "It is enough; now stay your hand." And the angel of the LORD was standing by the threshing floor of Ornan the Jebusite.* [16] *And David lifted his eyes and saw the angel of the LORD standing between earth and heaven, and in his hand a drawn sword stretched out over Jerusalem. Then David and the elders, clothed in sackcloth, fell upon their faces.* [17] *And David said to God, "Was it not I who gave command to number the people? It is I who have sinned and done great evil. But these sheep, what have they done? Please let your hand, O LORD my God, be against me and against my father's house. But do not let the plague be on your people."*
> 2 Chronicles 21:14-17

Whatever the answers to all the related theological questions might be, let's turn our attention now to the co-regency of David and Solomon. A co-regency period when both David and Solomon ruled is beyond question if we rely on the biblical evidence. 1 Kings 1-3, 1 Chronicles 23:1, and 29:22 show that David made Solomon king while David still lived. We are told that Solomon received two coronations, one when David made him King, and another after David died. The first coronation was to prevent Adonijah from usurping the throne. The second coronation happened when Solomon began his sole rule.

1 Chronicles tells us that David made preparations for the Temple, even though he could not be its builder. He made arrangements for building materials, for laborers, and for the priesthood and the Levites, the gate keepers, the treasurers and the other officials. He remained very much involved in his last days. Just the cedar, as well as the great amount of bronze required, could take months or even years to produce and to deliver. Lumber must be harvested and dried, in this case in Lebanon. Bronze must be made from copper which had to be mined and shipped. Only two places could begin to supply it all, Timna and Faynan. These materials alone were certainly not part of a regular inventory.

> [5] *For David said, "Solomon my son is young and inexperienced, and the house that is to be built for the LORD must be exceedingly magnificent, of fame and glory throughout all lands. I will therefore make preparation for it." So David provided materials in great quantity before his death.* 1 Chronicles 22:5

David's health began to decline. A young woman was brought to him for the sole purpose of keeping him warm, but his death was not immediate. David was still the King, and so was Solomon. How long did this co-regency continue? Estimates are from a few months to several years.

Solomon began his reign with the first coronation in 970 B.C., and David reigned with him for up to several more years until he died. Surely, David never stopped being concerned with the building of the Temple. David's census, and his sighting of the angel with its drawn sword belongs somewhere in this time period. David still had the authority to decide where the altar of the Temple would be, even if that meant a change of an already-established plan. Of course, if there really was no King David, or if he was just a tribal chieftain, we would not find him counting a great nation, because there was none. We would not find him or his son planning to build a great Temple, because there was no powerful, wealthy, administrative government to make that possible.

The sky furnishes evidence that this account is not legend, but truth. Further, it supplies us with a way to date the last days of David. The sky tells us what that angel's sword would be called in our time, and precisely when such a sword appeared above the city of Jerusalem.

Göran Henriksson of Uppsala University has retro-calculated the time of a stunning appearance of Comet Encke. It happened in the year 964 B.C. Encke is a comet which still orbits the earth each 3.3 years, but its appearance has allegedly changed. Henriksson asserts that Encke was very bright during the Bronze Age, but is so no longer. Others say there is no recorded appearance of Encke of which we may be sure before its discovery in 1786 (c.f. Brian G. Marsden and Zdenek Sekanina, "Comets and Nongravitational Forces. VI. Periodic Comet Encke 1786-1971" cited in Colin R. Nichol, *The Great Christ Comet*. Crossways, 2015.) But Henriksson has indexed the appearance of the comet to a rock carving in Sweden showing the comet with a solar eclipse. If he is right, this allows one appearance of the comet to be dated precisely. He is able to index appearances to other events precisely as well, so that the other times the comet was visible can be listed with a very high degree of certainty. Henriksson says Ephoros observed Encke's nucleus break into two comets around the year 371 B.C. This is part of the reason the comet appears different today.

The orbit of Encke in David's time was such that it appeared in the northern sky at Jerusalem's latitude. From the site of David's palace it would have appeared north in the direction of the threshing floor where David had formerly brought the Tabernacle. Henriksson's calculations have the comet with one end on the horizon over the threshing floor in 964 B.C., as seen from the location of the palace to the South. The comet would have appeared to be hanging in the sky above that threshing floor, which was then bought by David to become the place of the future Temple's altar. In this writer's opinion, the Comet Encke shows a high likelihood of being what David considered the drawn sword of the angel.

The year 964 seems late for David to have been still alive. 970 as the start of Solomon's reign has been established, and we have seen that another sky event, a solar eclipse, is perfectly consistent with that year as Solomon's first. The sky events argue that the sword in the sky was also an actual event claimed to be datable with great precision. The idea that David died shortly after Solomon became King may need to be revisited, based on the accumulating evidence which includes Comet Encke and the eclipse of 1406 B.C.

Halley's Comet is not on record before 241 B.C., so we cannot be sure it was even in our solar system earlier. That, like the argument against Encke's presence noted above, is an argument from silence, but an argument nevertheless. The orbital period of Halley's Comet is 76.1 years. This is an average, because the orbital period has ranged from 74.42 years (1835-1910) to as long as 79.25 years (451-530). If we add 1986 years (it appeared last in 1986 A.D.) and 970 years (the years B.C. when Solomon's reign began, in coregency with David), the total is 2956 years. Dividing this total by 76.1 gives 38.84. The sum is nearly evenly divisible by the average orbital period for Halley's Comet. This is by no means conclusive, of course, but Halley's should not be completely excluded from consideration as the sword witnessed by David.

When we look up, we see what we call a comet. When someone from the past looked up, he saw an angel's drawn sword.

The deeper truth about the circumstances associated with that event is not conveyed by any modern knowledge of comets. The truth is that David had sinned. What David believed he saw, interpreted by Gad the Seer, corresponds to the truth about David's guilt. Judah really was under the judgment of God. Was a comet really the sword of an angel? That interpretation of what David saw in the sky is correct in its own way. To see nothing but a comet misses the truth.

If Comet Encke was what David understood to be the drawn sword of the angel, we have confirmation of the chronology of David's life as determined from the Bible. The whole larger story of this time is affirmed as well. We have confirmation of what the Bible says about the level of political organization and wealth in Judah at that time. Everything about the story of David's rule as King is affirmed by the appearance of the comet. We have a reference datum in the comet which is in agreement with another precisely datable sky event, a solar eclipse, helping us cement our chronology as consistent with biblical evidence.

These are the kinds of discoveries that can emerge when the Bible meets the sky.

Chapter 2: King Hezekiah and the Sign of the Moving Shadow

"He trusted in the LORD, the God of Israel, so that there was none like him among all the kings of Judah after him, nor among those who were before him."
2 Kings 18:5

The Assyrian Threat

One of the most remarkable kings to occupy the throne of ancient Judah was Hazaqyah, Hezekiah. His name means: the Lord strengthens. Hezekiah was the son of Ahaz, a man who put his own interests and concerns ahead of faithfulness to God, and did great harm in the process. The sign of the moving shadow that we will explore in this chapter deserves a thorough introduction in order for us to understand the depth of the dire situation facing Hezekiah when his father died at age thirty-six. The sign spoke to that situation.

Hezekiah's father Ahaz lived in fear of Israel and Syria to the north. The kings of these two nations, Pekah and Rezin, threatened to force Ahaz into an alliance with them, because they feared the rising power of Assyria to the east led at that time by Tiglath-Pileser III.

All nations had reason to fear Assyria. The Assyrians were infamous for the intentional, sadistic cruelty they inflicted without exception upon the people they defeated. This viciousness was an essential part of their warfare, a type of terrorism that went before them. The stories told by witnesses made clear that if the armies of Assyria came into sight on the horizon, no worse future could be imagined.

The Assyrians were quite capable of engaging armies in the field, and even at sea, but much of their warfare was waged against walled cities. A high-ranking officer of the Assyrian army would approach the wall of the city and issue an ultimatum to the leaders within. There would be only one chance to surrender and live; that chance was now. Behind this threat was the fact that almost no city-state or nation had been able to stop the Assyrians in their quest for ever-greater power and territory.

At least one of three things would happen. (1) The people of the city would suffer hunger or starvation. (2) The Assyrians would breach the walls, undermine them by digging, or cross them with scaling ladders, and overtake the city. (3) An unforeseen deliverance would keep the Assyrians from their victory.

If the city leaders surrendered, they kept their lives, and people in the city were resettled in a different land, never to see their homes again. That was the least violent way the Assyrians ever conducted themselves, destroying hope and preventing the possibility of rebellion.

If the city's leaders did not surrender, hoping their gods would deliver them and trusting that they had enough grain and water inside, they were risking their own lives, as well as the lives of many more. Then, if Assyria's overwhelming numbers won their victory, there would be torture and mass killing. It would inevitably follow the siege.

The purpose of the city's defensive wall was to provide protection against enemies. But for how long could it hold them out? Inside were food stores kept against the threat of a siege. Water was indispensable as well. Unless water was available from a source within the city, it was kept in vessels that were bound in time to run out, just as the food was. Siege warfare was largely a matter of time...of waiting. Who could afford to wait longer, the aggressors or the defenders? For those inside a besieged city, the psychological pressure of the siege was horrendous.

From the city wall archers could shoot arrows down at the invaders, but there was little more anyone could do. The city gate had to remain barred against the enemy, and even if a company of defenders might have gone outside the city to fight, they would be no match for the superior numbers of Assyrians.

Soon siege towers, which the Assyrians had perfected and brought here on wheels, were fully assembled and rolled up against the city wall. These were actually multi-story armored buildings with battering rams inside. Soldiers within the towers were protected from arrows. Together they would swing the suspended rams until they pulverized the wall surface ahead of them.

When the moment came that the Assyrians gained entrance to the city, the torture and killing began which would make this city one more example of what happened to anyone who did not immediately surrender. Everyone had heard what the Assyrians did to their victims. The city leaders who had reached the decision not to surrender might be placed in iron cages suspended where all could see them, left there to die of exposure, starvation and thirst in full view. Others within the city were literally skinned alive. Still others were impaled on poles. Children and youth were exterminated in fires. Still others had eyelids cut off, or eyes gouged out, or noses and other body parts cut off. Some were beheaded.

Assyrian soldiers served one year with two years off. They tended all to be experienced in battle because of this. The extreme cruelty which they routinely practiced seems to have been so terrible that it even effected them. What we call Post Traumatic Stress Disorder may be at the root of stories from Assyrian soldiers who believed they were haunted by people they had tortured! ("The Assyrians — The Appalling Lords of Torture: Impalement, flaying, and amputations were the trademark of the Assyrians." Peter Preskar, Dec 27, 2020. Lessons from History https://medium.com/lessons-from-history/assyrians-torture-60fabb7a9642)

The Immanuel Sign

So Judah's King Ahaz, Hezekiah's father, found himself in the position of having to choose whom his enemies would be, Rezin and Pekah, or Tiglath-Pileser III of Assyria. Pekah and Rezin threatened Ahaz with destruction at their hands if Ahaz did not join their anti-Assyrian alliance. Assyria loomed as a threat on its way. It was at this time that God's prophet Isaiah was sent to Ahaz with a prophetic oracle and a sign. This king, who had actually closed the Temple doors, claimed his faith was sufficient so that he didn't need a sign. Isaiah told the pretentious king God would send a sign anyway! "Behold, a virgin will conceive and bear a son, and will call his name Immanuel (Isaiah 7:14.)" It's called today the Immanuel Sign. Christians connect it to the birth of Jesus many years later. Before Isaiah was finished, he told Ahaz that soon Rezin and Pekah would no longer be a threat; they would be gone, because the Lord was bringing the Assyrians on the scene.

It wasn't long before Isaiah's words proved true. The kingdoms of Israel and Syria were no more. Assyria had vanquished them. Ahaz even supplied troops for Assyria, and paid tribute to be a vassal state in lieu of being conquered like the rest. He remained a sell-out, transforming the worship of Yahweh as it had come down from Moses through Solomon.

> *[17] And King Ahaz cut off the frames of the stands and removed the basin from them, and he took down the sea from off the bronze oxen that were under it and put it on a stone pedestal. [18] And the covered way for the Sabbath that had been built inside the house and the outer entrance for the king he caused to go around the house of the LORD, because of the king of Assyria. [19] Now the rest of the acts of Ahaz that he did, are they not written in the Book of the Chronicles of the Kings of Judah? [20] And Ahaz slept with his fathers and was buried with his fathers in the city of David, and Hezekiah his son reigned in his place.*
>
> *2 Kings 16:17-20*

Ahaz was not the only sinful king in Judah's history, but he had become the worst. He even offered a son as a human sacrifice to the idol Moloch (2 Kings 16:3)! This was strictly forbidden in the Law (Leviticus 18:21), but Ahaz was devoted to syncretism, not to Israel's God alone. We do not know that son's name, but he might have been king one day if the circumstances had been right. Hezekiah was the son that lived.

In such an atmosphere as this, Ahaz' son Hezekiah emerges as an astonishing contrast to the religious corruption of his father. When Tiglath-Pileser III's successor Sargon II died, Hezekiah revolted against Assyria. He stopped paying tribute to the new Assyrian king, Sennacherib. He began to prepare Jerusalem for a siege. His workers cut the famous tunnel through rock beneath the city to bring water inside from a hidden source outside the wall, the Gihon Spring. The Siloam Inscription was found at the meeting point where workers met other workers tunneling from the other direction. Water would now be always present inside the city.

Hezekiah had at least secured that. He set out to maintain stores of grain as well.

Hezekiah was not only a king with strategic interests for his city's defense. More than that he was a religious reformer. He restored the proper ceremonies within the Temple, and destroyed the altars and high places approved by his unfaithful father. Hezekiah would trust the God of Israel, and he would believe the prophets such as Isaiah, rather than ignore them as his father had done.

Hezekiah had surely taken action against Assyria their king would not tolerate. Both Israel and Syria had only recently fallen, though they were united against Assyria. Judah was small by comparison. No other king or nation had stopped the Assyrian advance. The chances of Hezekiah's success in practical, worldly terms were nonexistent. It was only a matter of time now before the Assyrian army would appear on the horizon, coming this time for Jerusalem and Hezekiah.

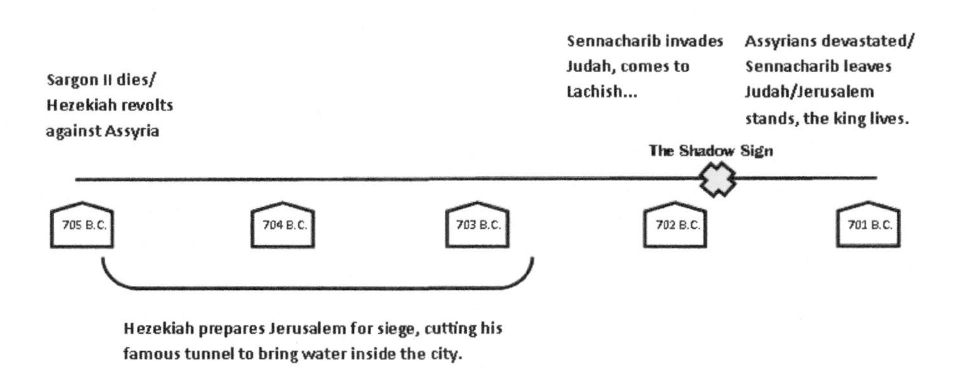

Figure 2. Hezekiah timeline.

That day soon arrived. Thousands of Assyrian soldiers in their characteristic conical helmets of bronze stood in the distance. The Rabshakeh, cupbearer to the king, rode up to the wall of Jerusalem. His ultimatum came in the language of the people in order to terrify them all. These people inside knew that Hezekiah's new tunnel would provide them with water in case of a siege, but the Rabshakeh's threat, that they were doomed to drink their own urine and eat their own dung (2 Kings 18:27), must still have been chilling.

No city official gave the Rabshakeh an answer. The King was not present among them. Then the Rabshakeh claimed Judah's own God, Yahweh, had sent the Assyrians. How futile would resistance be against their own God?! But that attempt to sow fear was not enough for the Rabshakeh; he then proceeded to revile and blaspheme Yahweh himself.

This was the same Yahweh who three centuries earlier had assured King David that he would maintain this city and its throne in the hands of David's descendants. True, the people had proven unfaithful, as had their kings. They had proven unworthy of that promise. But Isaiah's words, and the sign from heaven we are about to consider now, surely meant that Yahweh was keeping that promise anyway. It is important to understand that Hezekiah was a king from David's line.

The Rabshakeh finally left the city wall with no answer from Hezekiah. The sun set on the tents of the Assyrian camp with its thousands of battle-hardened sadist-soldiers waiting for Sennacherib himself to arrive from the siege of nearby Lachish.

When the sun rose the next morning the Assyrian camp was eerily silent, motionless. During the night the would-be killers had died in their tents. Swiftly, unexpectedly, the Assyrian threat was broken. Sennacherib never arrived at Jerusalem. His plans changed suddenly. He returned to his home where he was later assassinated. In his boasting about his conquests Sennacherib could only claim that he shut up Hezekiah "like a bird in a cage" on the Taylor Prism.

The historian Herodatus, writing around 450 B.C., described a somewhat similar event happening in Egypt between the Assyrian and Egyptian armies. The Assyrian camp was overrun by mice that ate components of their weapons, such as bow strings, leaving the Assyrians unable to fight. Some consider this report to be an adaption of the actual biblical event in Jerusalem.

Berossus, a transplanted Babylonian in Greece, writing in the Third Century B.C., corroborates our biblical texts in these words preserved by Josephus:

> "Now when Sennacherib was returning from his Egyptian war to Jerusalem, he found his army under Rabshakeh his general in danger [by a plague, for] God had sent a pestilential distemper upon his army: and on the very first night of the siege an hundred fourscore and five thousand, with their captains and generals, were destroyed. So the King was in a great dread, and in a terrible agony at this calamity; and being in great fear for his whole army, he fled with the rest of his forces to his own Kingdom, and to his city Nineveh. And when he had abode there a little while, he was treacherously assaulted, and died by the hands of his elder sons Adrammelech and Sarasar: and was slain in his own temple, which was called Araske. Now these sons of his were driven away on account of the murder of their father by the citizens, and went into Armenia. While Assarachoddas took the Kingdom of Sennacherib." And this proved to be the conclusion of this Assyrian expedition against the people of Jerusalem." (Quoted by Josephus, Antiquities of the Jews, Book X, Chapter 1, paragraph 4 & 5).

The Sign

All this is the background for the sign we are considering in this chapter. Such were the stakes; they could be no higher! Now let us look carefully at the biblical text, 2 Kings 20:1-11. This is where we find the story of the moving shadow, and also in Isaiah 38:1-22, with mention in 2 Chronicles 32:24.

> *In those days Hezekiah became sick and was at the point of death. And Isaiah the prophet the son of Amoz came to him and said to him, "Thus says the LORD, 'Set your house in order, for you shall die; you shall not recover.'"[2] Then Hezekiah turned his face to the wall and prayed to the LORD, saying, [3] "Now, O LORD, please remember how I have walked before you in faithfulness and with a whole heart, and have done what is good in your sight." And Hezekiah wept bitterly. [4] And before Isaiah had gone out of the middle court, the word of the LORD came to him: [5] "Turn back, and say to Hezekiah the leader of my people, Thus says the LORD, the God of David your father: I have heard your prayer; I have seen your tears. Behold, I will heal you. On the third day you shall go up to the house of the LORD, [6] and I will add fifteen years to your life. I will deliver you and this city out of the hand of the king of Assyria, and I will defend this city for my own sake and for my servant David's sake." [7] And Isaiah said, "Bring a cake of figs. And let them take and lay it on the boil, that he may recover."*
>
> *[8] And Hezekiah said to Isaiah, "What shall be the sign that the LORD will heal me, and that I shall go up to the house of the LORD on the third day?" [9] And Isaiah said, "This shall be the sign to you from the LORD, that the LORD will do the thing that he has*

promised: shall the shadow go forward ten steps, or go back ten steps?" [10] *And Hezekiah answered, "It is an easy thing for the shadow to lengthen ten steps. Rather let the shadow go back ten steps."* [11] *And Isaiah the prophet called to the* LORD, *and he brought the shadow back ten steps, by which it had gone down on the steps of Ahaz.*

The Order of Events

Reading the text in order, it may seem that the story of God's miraculous defense of Jerusalem in 2 Kings 19 had already happened before Hezekiah's illness and the accompanying sign. But we have two reasons to think otherwise.

First, the text begins: "In those days…" This is a general time reference that does not require the story of Hezekiah's miraculous healing to follow the deliverance of the city.

Second, the Lord says through Isaiah to Hezekiah, "…and I will add fifteen years to your life. I will deliver you and this city out of the hand of the king of Assyrian, and I will defend this city for my own sake and for my servant David's sake (v. 6)." It certainly seems that Hezekiah's illness preceded the attempted siege.

This means that the sign given Hezekiah was first of all a confirmation that he would continue to live, but second, a confirmation that Jerusalem would not fall to Assyria. After all, what difference would it have made for Hezekiah to recover if that only meant death or imprisonment at the hands of the Assyrians? So, while the sign is specifically related to Hezekiah's recovery, it means still more. It means Hezekiah must not surrender, but faithfully stand firm against the Sennacherib's armies.

When the Assyrian horde came up to the wall of Jerusalem from the north, Hezekiah had already received the sign from the Lord. That is what we must conclude if we read the text carefully.

Looking More Closely

The sign offered to King Hezekiah involved a movement of the normal shadow in a direction contrary to nature. Numerous attempts have been made to explain this apparent backward motion of the sun's shadow. There are those who say we must not do that, because it amounts to questioning God or the Bible. Others have said an instant reversal of the earth's rotation, with no noticeable effects to anyone or anything on the earth's surface despite that sudden stop, is the explanation of what happened. For those intent on denying all miracles, this story is just another tale.

We might mention here Camille Flammarion, a French thinker whose thoughts led him to diverse areas of interest. One of those areas was astronomy. In 1885 Flammarion published an article about a particular sundial in the Observatory of Juvisy in Paris. By adjusting the angle of the base of the sundial, Flammarion was able to achieve a retrogression of the sun's shadow. This is just one of the attempts by researchers to take seriously the 2 Kings account and move toward an explanation of how it may have happened. The great difficulty with Flammarion's attempt is that it requires the actual manipulation of an unheard-of kind of sundial.

In the early years of the 20th Century the famous astronomer E. W. Maunder took up this matter as well, attempting to show by mathematics that a retreat of the shadow on a sundial was possible.

Does God use only the supernatural in the working of signs, miracles? Is the natural supernatural already, since God made the natural too? Is it wrong to explore the ways God may have brought about this event, or is this rather a kind of praise that comes from believing the Bible first of all, and hoping to discover more? This is something for you, the reader, to decide. This is one of those places where the Bible meets the sky.

The *Ma'aloth*

Are we to think of the shadow moving on a sundial or on a stairway? Translators are making a choice between these options when they translate *ma'aloth*. They have no way of being certain what it meant to the writer. Apparently, that writer already knew what the *ma'aloth* of Ahaz were, and it seems his first audience did also, because he sees no need to explain it. But that knowledge is now lost to us. All we can do is attempt to understand by creating possible scenarios and eliminating others.

A sundial of some kind is certainly within the range of acceptable meanings for ma'aloth. Sundials and sun clocks predate Hezekiah. They have been found in Egypt from about 1500 B.C., and in Ukraine from about 1300 B.C. Mesopotamian knowledge of how to use the sun's shadow to indicate time is attested for this period as well. In fact, Mesopotamian astronomers divided the sky into 360 degree intervals, and used this 360-division system for reckoning day and night, watches within them, and half-watches.

The principle of the sundial is simple. As the sun moves across the sky from East to West through the daylight hours, the shadow it casts from a fixed post moves in the opposite direction. By indexing the positions of the shadow to the times of the day, ancient people could mark the passing of time. This was for general use, not precise. It served to give a simple, visible measurement of the working hours of the day.

The word sundial brings to mind a horizontal disc with numbers around the perimeter, and an upright angled piece called the gnomon to cast the shadow on the disc. That's how we envision it, but it is only one form the sun clock has taken, and from a time later than our event.

Earlier, in Egypt, one type of sun clock consisted of a short horizontal bar casting its shadow along a longer bar extending from beneath the short bar and perpendicular to it. Another type was a stone with a concave depression cut in it. A gnomon was set in the center of the diameter line. Marks inscribed on the concave surface marked the hours.

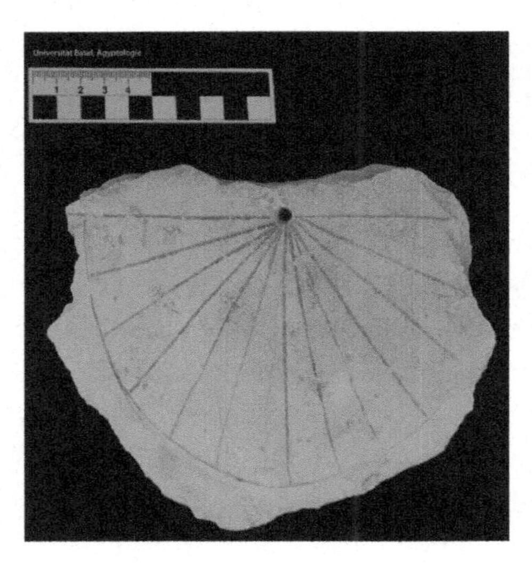

Figure 3.

Ancient Egyptian sundial with a socket for the gnomen (absent), and twelve divisions for hours, each divided in half by a dot. This dial was made from limestone, and it served as the model for another sun dial used in experiments to track shadow movement. (See Experiment section.) Photo supplied by: University of Basel / Public domain.

The concepts of minutes, and seconds, which are part of our everyday experience were not developed yet when early sun clocks were in use. They were not necessary to mark the work day. However, as the North-South ranges of the shadow changed with the seasons it became possible with a sun clock to find the days of the year with the shortest and longest amounts of daylight, and darkness. The midpoints between these, counted in days, were the equinoxes. Ahaz and Hezekiah lived at a time when time-measuring was still primitive, but somewhat developed.

Whatever the ma'aloth were, steps or sundial divisions, we may be confident they were not subdivided into impractical, small increments. Subdivisions were of a useful, practical nature.

If the ma'aloth were steps on a staircase they may have been built intentionally for this purpose, or else the time-keeping function of the ma'aloth was an accidental consequence of its location and orientation. Israeli archaeologist Yigael Yadin hypothesized that ma'aloth were built into the lines of buildings as steps that could measure time by means of the moving shadow from the sun. This idea actually comes from a small, Egyptian sun clock. No separate gnomon is necessary for this kind of clock.

Below: Egyptian sun clock photo used under terms of GNU General Public License.

Right: Drawing from Y. Yadin. "The Dial of Ahaz" / זחא תולעמ." *Eretz-Israel: Archaeological, Historical and Geographical Studies* / (1958): 91-96. Accessed May 6, 2021. http://www.jstor.org/stable/23612438.

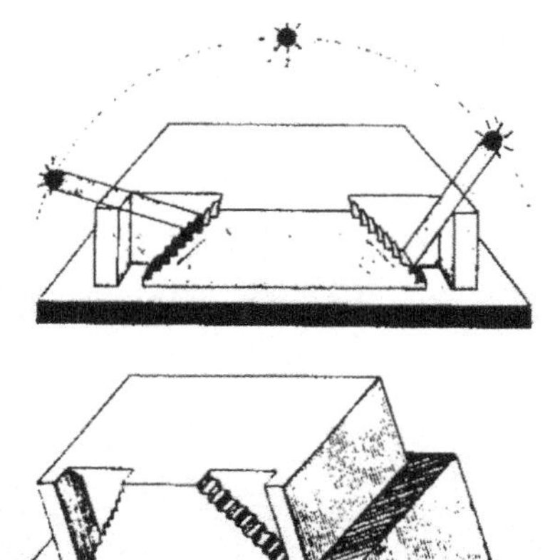

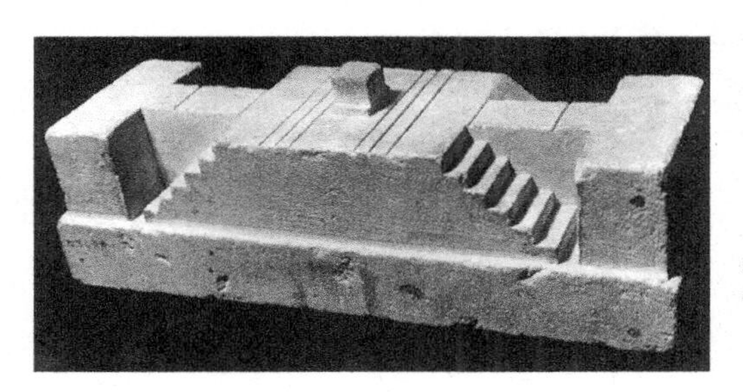

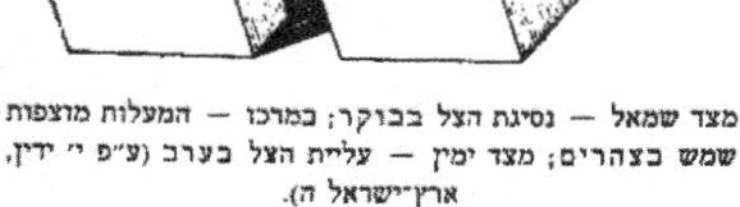

Figure 4.

If we look to the text for our information, the ma'aloth seem to be within view for Hezekiah and Isaiah as they are meeting in the palace. Hezekiah is confined there by his illness. The sign is to assure him that in three days he will be able to go up to the Temple, meaning he is too sick to leave now. If the sign of the moving shadow was only reported to Hezekiah by someone who saw it somewhere else, it would have lost some of its dramatic sign power. Hezekiah was to see it himself. That is the plain sense of the text.

With this in mind we can draw upon what is held by the great majority to be the locations of the palace and the Temple. The first royal palace stood on the northern end of the old City of David. To the north, and higher in elevation, was the threshing floor of Araunah the Jebusite. David had brought the Ark of the Covenant there to rest within the Tabernacle.

David's son Solomon replaced the Tabernacle with a permanent, grand Temple. He also built a new palace complex north of where David's had been. This palace continued to serve the kings of Judah in years to come until Hezekiah replaced it with another palace to the west. The Temple remained as the highest building, and at the highest elevation. *This means that whatever Hezekiah saw, he saw from his sick room in the palace. It must have been either in a courtyard of the palace, or outside the Temple.*

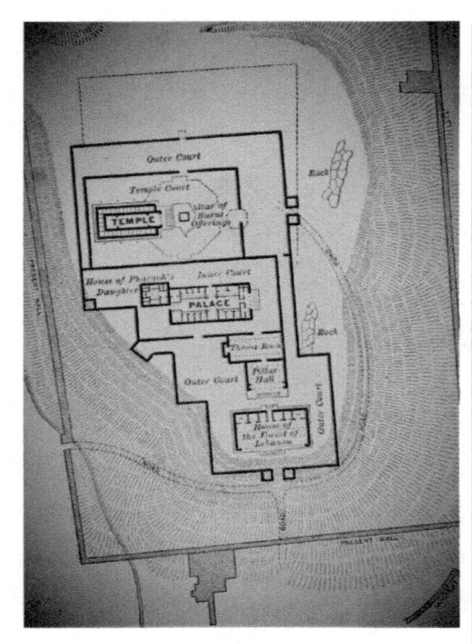

Figure 5.

One of numerous drawings of the Temple and Palace complexes in Jerusalem. The Temple Court was higher than the Palace; someone in the palace could see the Temple Court through windows. If the *ma'aloth* of Ahaz were something installed in the Temple Court, they should have been visible to Hezekiah and Isaiah in the Palace. If the ma'aloth were part of sun a clock in the Palace Courts, they should have been visible in the Palace there as well. From: A History of all Nations from the Earliest Times; Being a Universal Historical Library, 1905. Author: Wright, John Henry, 1852-1908. Publisher: [Philadelphia, New York : Lea Brothers & Company. Contributing Library: University of California Libraries. Digitizing Sponsor: Internet Archive. No known copyright restrictions.

We know of items Ahaz removed from the Temple in addition to changes he made to existing fixtures. There is only one addition to the Temple we know of ordered by Ahaz.

> [10] *When King Ahaz went to Damascus to meet Tiglath-pileser king of Assyria, he saw the altar that was at Damascus. And King Ahaz sent to Uriah the priest a model of the altar, and its pattern, exact in all its details.* [11] *And Uriah the priest built the altar; in accordance with all that King Ahaz had sent from Damascus, so Uriah the priest made it, before King Ahaz arrived from Damascus.* [12] *And when the king came from Damascus, the king viewed the altar. Then the king drew near to the altar and went up on it* [13] *and burned his burnt offering and his grain offering and poured his drink offering and threw the blood of his peace offerings on the altar.* [14] *And the bronze altar that was before the LORD he removed from the front of the house, from the place between his altar and the house of the LORD, and put it on the north side of his altar.* [15] *And King Ahaz commanded Uriah the priest, saying, "On the great altar burn the morning burnt offering and the evening grain offering and the king's burnt offering and his grain offering, with the burnt offering of all the people of the land, and their grain offering and their drink offering. And throw on it all the blood of the burnt offering and all the blood of the sacrifice, but the bronze altar shall be for me to inquire by."* [16] *Uriah the priest did all this, as King Ahaz commanded. 2 Kings 16:10-16*

Might the ma'aloth of Ahaz have been the steps up to this altar? Certainly, this is only one hypothetical possibility. But combining Yadin's suggestion about steps with the altar from Damascus yields a possibility that would surely have been visible to anyone looking from the palace to the Temple.

A Partial Solar Eclipse

The story of the sign involves a short time span. (1) Isaiah delivers the word from the Lord that Hezekiah will not survive his illness. (2) Even before he can leave the palace, Isaiah is sent back to Hezekiah with another message in answer to Hezekiah's secret prayer. (3) Hezekiah is told that he will be able to go to the Temple in just three days. (4) The sign for all this will happen now, not after those three days, or at some other future time. The plain sense of the text is that the sign took place then, just as soon as Hezekiah had made his choice about which direction the shadow should move on the steps, forward or backward.

The sign was the assurance that Hezekiah would live another fifteen years. With that our biblical investigation finds a most-important clue which allows us to move forward toward a further understanding of how this sign may have come about.

Hezekiah died in 687 B.C. Since the sign confirmed that Hezekiah would live fifteen more years, it would have occurred in 702 B.C. We discover that a partial solar eclipse was visible over Israel on March 5 of that year.

The Eclipse of March 5, 702 B.C.

On the 5th of March in 702 B.C., eclipse 03083 (the catalog number from NASA's Five Millennia of Solar Eclipses) subtracted 70 percent of the sun's light from the surface of the earth in Israel. The computer tools available to even the amateur sky student today allow recreating this eclipse on a screen, just as it happened. In Israel the greatest extent of the eclipse happened shortly before midday. The sun was not high overhead, but about 45 degrees from the horizon. The direction of the moon's travel across the sun's surface was from west to east.

While there is no proof that this eclipse was involved in the sign of the moving shadow, the simple fact that it happened fifteen years before Hezekiah's death, coupled with the rarity and the wondrous nature of eclipses in general, makes this an event of great interest.

Might there have been a way that an eclipse could move the shadow backward on a sundial of some kind? The answer is: yes. See A Simple Possibility below. But this would require the number of *ma'aloth* between midday and early morning to be ten. If the sundial device, whatever kind it was, had ten divisions between midday and early morning, the change in light and shadow on these *ma'aloth* might be read as a retreat of the shadow ten *ma'aloth.* The stairs as suggested by Yadin look promising here. Ten steps, as in his drawing, does seem to be a reasonable number for movement from one floor to another.

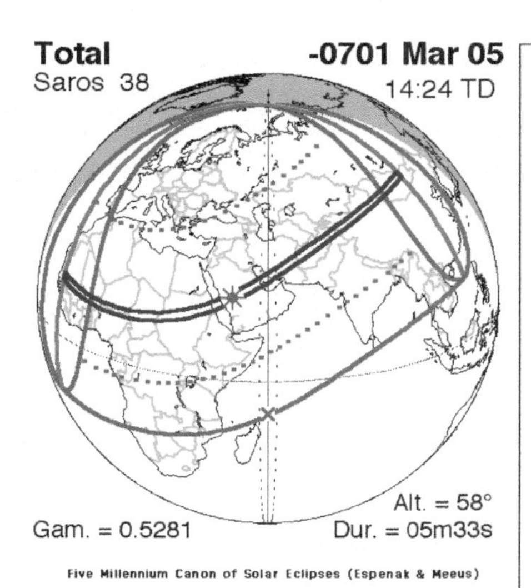

Figure 6.

This diagram shows the path of the March 5 eclipse. Source: Five Millennium Canon of Solar Eclipses, NASA. This site also provides the following information about the eclipse itself: From a vantage point in Jerusalem the intensity obscuration for this event was 64.5%; magnitude 0.708; altitude 45.6 degrees; azimuth 183.7 degrees; start of the partial eclipse 7:24:16 UTC; end of partial eclipse 10:02:48 UTC; maximum eclipse 8:41:55 UTC.

Figure 7. This illustrates the position of the sky at the greatest extent of the eclipse. Source: Stellarium.

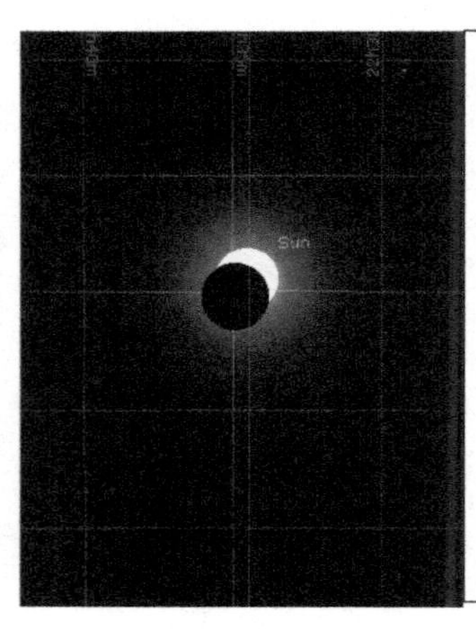

Figure 8. This illustration is a Stellarium close-up of the March 5 eclipse at its greatest extent as seen from Jerusalem. The motion of the moon across the sun was from right to left, and slightly upward. About 70% of the sunlight was blocked from the earth due to the eclipse, but not from the areas to each side where parhelia might occur. See below. The article cited from Applied Optics offers proof that the return of post-eclipse sunlight and the appearances of parhelia are not necessarily simultaneous. In other words, sudden light source shifts are possible in these circumstances.

Parhelia

Another phenomenon of interest to us in this context is the parhelion, the sundog. These appear in the sky as false suns or rainbow sections which can be on one or both sides of the sun. They can be faint, and they can be bright. In optimum circumstances arcs of light appear with them, and additional false suns appear above and/or below the sun. Parhelia can appear anywhere on earth at any time of year, though they are rare. They are more typically seen closer to the poles, because they are formed by ice crystals in the upper atmosphere. The optical physics which produce parhelia are constant, as one would expect. Each false sun will be twenty-two degrees from the real sun. So, the arc of the sky encompassed by two parhelia is forty-four degrees.

Parhelia can be extremely bright. I have observed this personally; I remember a time when I was outdoors playing as a child. The sun seemed brighter than it had ever been, and I looked up to see three of them that were indistinguishable in brightness.

Figure 9.

Here is one striking example of parhelic circle with bright lateral parhelia.

Credit: NASA/Lora Koenig, Public Domain

Figure 10. This photo was taken with a camera oriented vertically at the Dead Sea, demonstrating that a parhelic circle can form in the most unexpected places, including Israel. Photo courtesy Koby Harati.

Figure 11.

The German words on this painting from a book published in 1550 say: "In 1533, three suns shone similarly as if they had fiery clouds around them, and they stood over the city of Münster, as if the city and the houses were burning, as painted here."

— in: *Augsburger Wunderzeichenbuch* — *Folio 131, c. 1550*

On March 27, 1703, parhelia were reported to change the shadow on sundials in Metz, France. Hampshire, England, experienced a similar phenomenon on March 28, 1848. The time change indicated on the sundials was one and one half hours each time. (Bible Fellowship Union, Bible Study Monthly vol. 85, no. 3, May 1, 2008). It is interesting that both these events are reported to have happened in March. While not a cold winter month, March still offers opportunities for cold atmospheric conditions at high altitudes.

If parhelia appeared over Jerusalem resulting in multiple light sources shining upon the ma'aloth of Ahaz, we must recognize that this could have been the mechanism of the miracle.

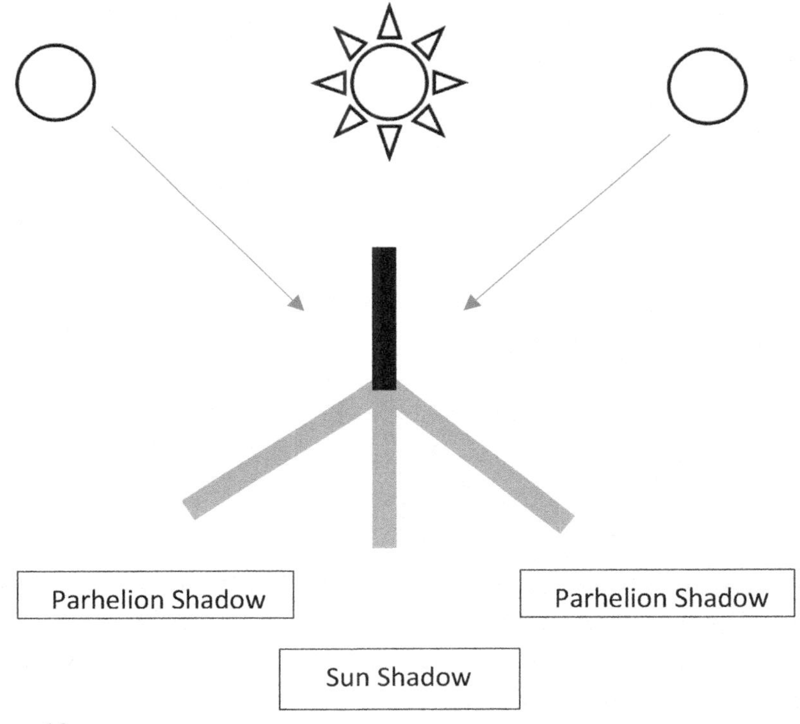

Figure 12.

One Simple Possibility

We can say this much with simple certainty: If a solar eclipse suddenly darkens the surface of the earth, the returning light that comes immediately afterward will restore shadows to where they appeared before. If the sun had moved to a place where its shadow fell ten ma'aloth from the beginning of the scale when a solar eclipse occurred, the result would be experienced as (1) normal shadows on the ma'aloth, (2) the shadows of early morning returning, overtaking all the ma'aloth, and (3) the shadow returning the ten ma'aloth to where it had been before. This is one simple explanation of how the sign might have happened. This particular means of reversing the shadow would be possible on any type of sun clock, providing that ten divisions comprised the distance between the late morning eclipse and the early morning or late evening shadows.

Eclipse with Parhelia

There is a further possibility to consider, the combination of parhelia with a solar eclipse. Why complicate the investigation this way by supposing something so rare? The answer will become apparent. The effect of a solar eclipse happening simultaneously with a parhelion has now been observed, studied, and photographed. (See: Gunther P. Können, Glenn Schneider, Evan H. Zucker, and Panu Lahtinen, "Subsuns and rainbows during solar eclipses," Applied Optics 59, F1-F10 [2020] © The Optical Society. Adapted with permission.)

This parhelion was actually below the sun in this case, a subsun, but it was caused the same way as a lateral parhelion as ice crystals refracted sunlight. It appeared as a subsun because the vantage point from which it was photographed was an aircraft at high altitude so that the location of ice crystals which caused the subsun was in a clouds appearing below the sun.

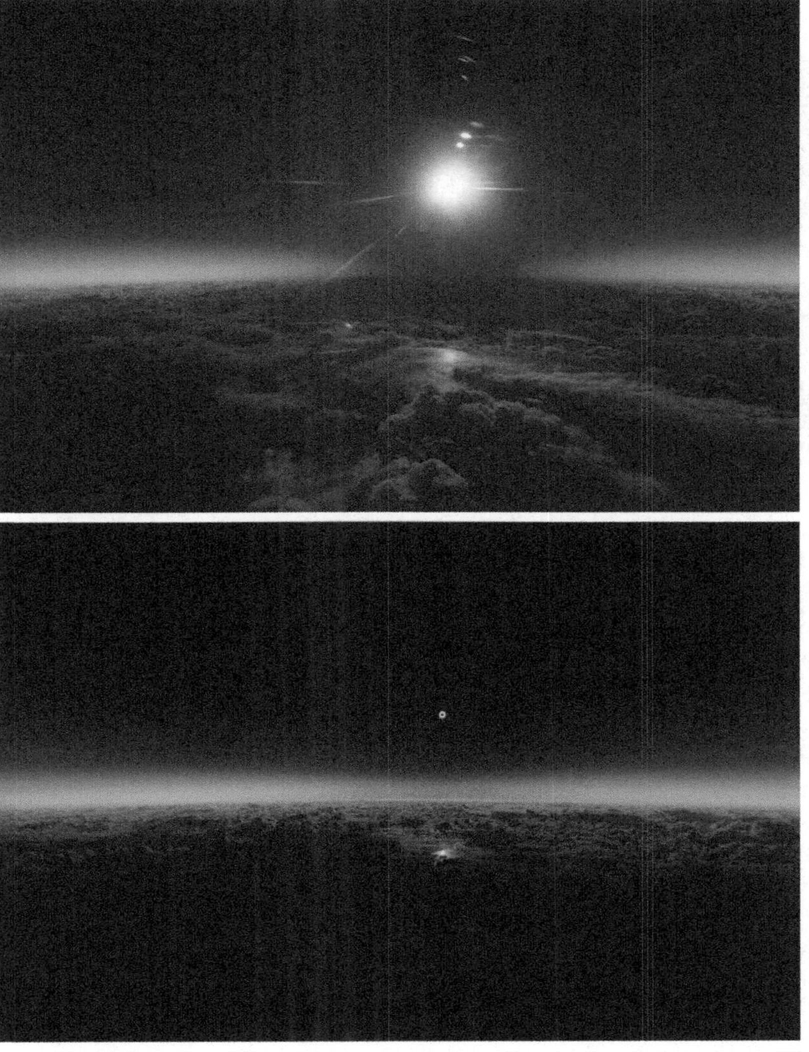

Fig. 12. Top: pretotality. The white spot straight under the Sun is the subsun. The dark patch on the clouds under the Sun is the rapidly approaching lunar umbra. The green spot is an artifact due to internal reflections in the camera lens (frame ID #3668, taken 28 s before totality). Bottom: During the final moments of totality, the subsun reappeared superimposed upon the clouds below that are already directly lit by the solar photospheric light (frame ID #3734, taken 2 s before totality ended). Pictures taken by Evan Zucker, 9 March 2016 (UTC); horizontal field of view is 115#. (Reproduced from: Gunther P. Können, Glenn Schneider, Evan H. Zucker, and Panu Lahtinen, "Subsuns and rainbows during solar eclipses," Applied Optics 59, F1-F10 [2020]).

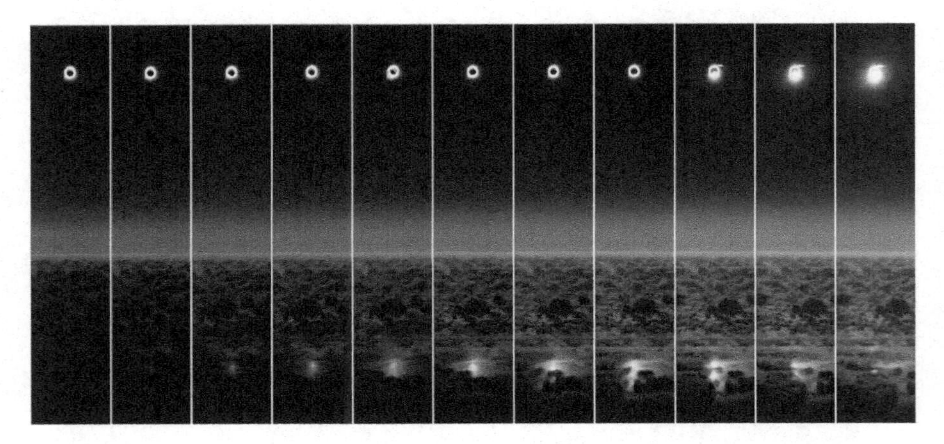

Fig. 13. Shortly before the end of totality, the light returns at the subsun point. Third contact (C3) occurs at the eighth frame of this composite consisting of 11 frames. The individual frames are mutually separated by 2 s; the 20 s sequence runs from C3–14 s until C3 + 6 s (frame ID #s 3728–3738). At this aircraft height (10.7 km), the horizon is depressed by ←·3.2# and is thus angularly closer to the subsun point than to the Sun. With the Sun 10.1# above the true horizon at C3, the line-of-site distance from the aircraft to the subsun point at sea level is←·62 km. (Reproduced from: Gunther P. Können, Glenn Schneider, Evan H. Zucker, and Panu Lahtinen, "Subsuns and rainbows during solar eclipses," Applied Optics 59, F1-F10 [2020]).

As the sun disappeared behind the moon, ***the subsun still momentarily shone.*** A light source other than the sun was shining from a different direction as the sun went dark. Let's transfer that idea to a parhelion horizontal from the sun as seen from the ground. Bear in mind that the eclipse of March 5, 702 B.C., was partial, not total. But the same optical physics should apply to parhelia, even if the sun was not completely eclipsed by the moon. ***In other words, a darkening of the eclipsed sun would not necessarily eliminate the sun-related light sources to the sides of the sun and the shadows they cast on the ground from their angular distances. Changes in shadow placements might last for multiple seconds.***

Figure 14. The sun with parhelia at 22 degrees to each side.

Figure 15. The sun being eclipsed by the moon during parhelia conditions. The encroaching shadow from the moon disc blocks the parhelion on the right. One light source only now shines on the earth, 22 degrees from the left of the sun. The shadow swings 22 degrees on the ground from where it had been when the sun was the primary light source. This would bring the shadow backward, rather than forward, as requested by Hezekiah.

Figure 16. As the moon disc continues to cross the sun, the right parhelion is no longer blocked while the left parhelion becomes blocked. Suddenly the light source on the ground is from 22 degrees right of the sun, 44 degrees from where the other parhelion had just shone. The shadow on the ground swings to the left, 22 degrees from where the sun's shadow had just been, and 44 degrees from where the other parhelion's shadow had been.

Experiments

Experiments were performed to study the phenomenon of the retreating shadow with different models of sun clock devices.

Care was taken to photograph the models at the appropriate times corresponding with the positions of the false suns, and the real sun. Below are some of the results of these experiments.

Eclipse alone

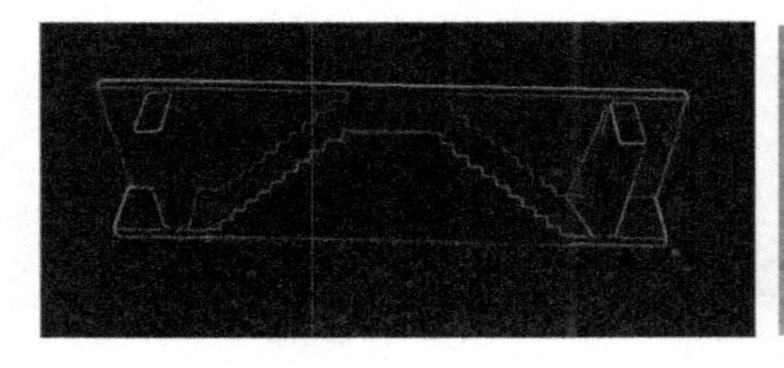

Figure 17. Stairway. **Figure 18. (same as left photo in Figure 20.)**

The stairway model did not produce a ten-step shadow change from the parhelia angled light sources, but it still fulfills the ten-step change in another way, provided there are ten steps on each side as in Yadin's drawing. As the eclipse stopped the sunlight at 12:40 P.M., the entire stairway suddenly took on the shadows of early morning; it was engulfed in darkness (**Stairway Figure 17**). Then, with the return of the sunlight following the eclipse, the steps appeared again as they had in **Stairway Figure 18**. This would have fulfilled the requirement of the retreat of the shadow ten steps from mid-day back to early morning.

Eclipse with parhelia

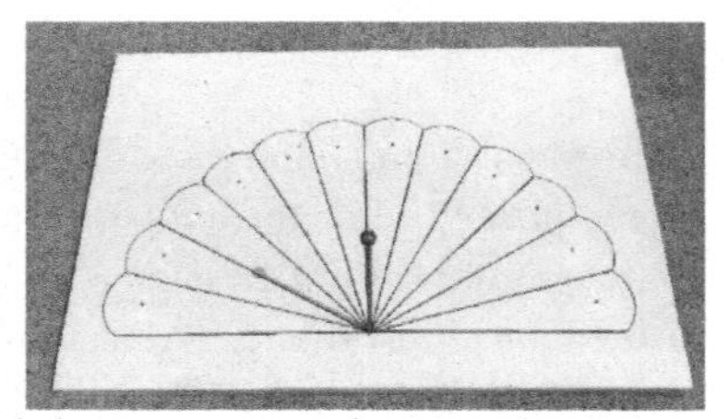

Figure 19. Models of the ten-step stairway and the Egyptian-style vertical gnomon sundial photographed at 11:10 A.M., with light direction from the location of the eastern false sun.

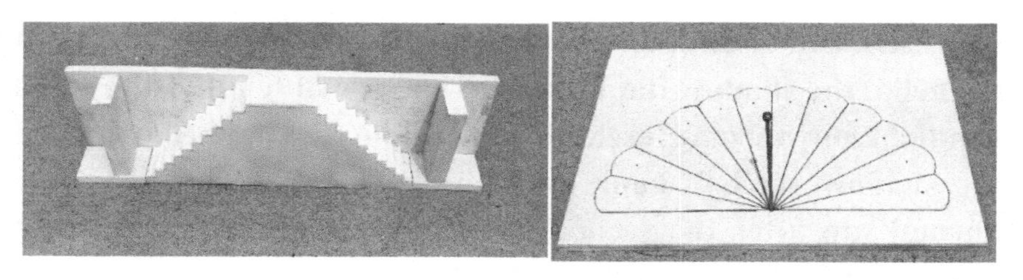

Figure 20. Models photographed at 12:40 P.M., with light direction from the actual sun, the partial eclipse in progress.

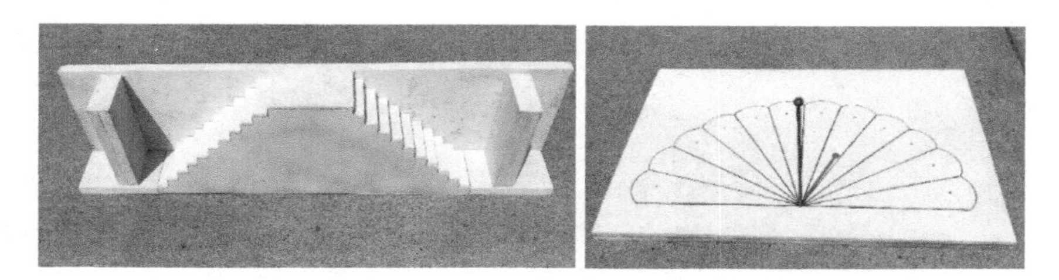

Figure 21. Models photographed at 2:10 P.M., with light direction from the direction of the western false sun.

Some Findings

The Egyptian-style sundial would have registered shadows in the order of **Figure 20**, **Figure 19**,, and **Figure 21.** This is because the moon crossed the sun from the west, first cutting off the sunlight forming the western parhelion, and leaving the eastern parhelion to shine. Then, as the moon passed the sun, the reverse happened—the light to the eastern parhelion was cut off, leaving the western parhelion. The resulting movement of the shadow was first backward on the dial, then forward, and then back to normal.

The Egyptian sun clock after which this model was made had twelve one-hour divisions, with a dot in each division to divide it in half. **The shadow movements covered ten of these half-hour**

segments. Under our simulated conditions of partial eclipse with parhelia, the shadow did in fact go backward ten divisions on a sundial known from Hezekiah's time. The first parhelion moved the shadow six half-hour divisions backward. The return of normal sun after the second parhelion accounted for another four divisions backward, for a total of ten.

A Most Interesting Discovery

Figure 22. The Hezekiah bulla discovered by Professor Eilat Mazar of the Hebrew University's Departement of Archaeology in 2015. Notice the ankh symbols, the downturned wings, and the three objects beneath the sun.

In 2015 Professor Eilat Mazar recovered a small seal from the Ophel area in Jerusalem, just south of where the First and Second Temples stood on Mt. Moriah. The seal was only one centimeter across. It was used to stamp clay with an impression identifying its owner; this is how scrolls were sealed as a wet clay ball would be formed over cords tying the scrolls closed. A winged sun disc appeared on the seal, with an ankh symbol on the right and on the left, the ankh being the symbol for life. Three straight items protruded from the sun as though the sun were on top of them. They appeared to have ball-shaped lower ends.

The name on the seal was at first misread. It was carefully stored, and only later did archaeologists realize that the letters actually said: Belonging to Hezekiah, son of Ahaz, King of Judah. This was not the first Hezekiah seal claimed to have been found, but it was the first whose chain of custody was proven to originate in an archaeological setting. The rest came from antiquities dealers and could not be absolutely proven authentic.

Now there could be no doubt that Hezekiah lived as a real King of Judah, just as the Bible says. Close to this seal another was discovered, the seal of the prophet Isaiah!

Other seals believed to belong to Hezekiah carried a different symbol, a dung beetle with wings circling upward around the edge. Something caused Hezekiah to change his symbol at a particular point in his life. The ankh symbols—two of them, not just one—suggest that Hezekiah wished to emphasize or celebrate his life. That might be expected from one who came close to dying from an incurable illness.

It has been observed that the wings of the sun disc on the seal are pointed downward, which is unprecedented for the winged sun disc symbol. Can this be unintentional, or does this also represent something, such as the perceived backward motion of the sun? Of course, we cannot know that these interpretations were intended by Hezekiah, representing his gift of fifteen more years of life. However, the three straight items coming from underneath the sun disc are in the same configuration as the shadows on a gnomon-style sundial at the times of approximately noon, and ninety minutes before and after noon, just as our parhelia proposal requires. The claim that these lines are rays fails to explain their overlapping, and the round objects on the lower ends. A ball at the end of a gnomon at least gives us some answer as to why these balls are present. Rays in Egyptian art have points rather than round ends.

What it Means

Have we simply "explained away" the miracle of the moving shadow by referencing a solar eclipse and rare atmospheric conditions? Absolutely not! God knows what we need before we ask, and begins to answer our requests already then (Isaiah 65:24; Matthew 6:8). God can arrange events, time events, orchestrate events long in advance, and guide humans to the particular moment and place to observe his works. Make no mistake about this attempt to discover the "how" of an act of God. If this was indeed how God brought about the movement of the shadow on the ma'aloth of Ahaz, it must be seen as a most exquisite and extraordinary supernatural use of the natural. It remains a miracle, nothing less.

What we have done here is to put the person who would deny this biblical account in the uncomfortable position of being unable to do that now. There can no longer be any doubt that Hezekiah was a real individual, and no longer a doubt that a solar eclipse happened some fifteen years before Hezekiah died. Even the most ardent skeptic cannot deny these facts. Further, we have shown the extreme plausibility of a combination of parhelia with a solar eclipse resulting in a backward-moving shadow, just as in the biblical text.

Having found a solar eclipse in the right year to lend support to the biblical story, and having gathered information about this eclipse available to us from NASA, we have been able to reproduce a backward movement of a sundial shadow to match that in the biblical account by applying optical mathematics. The combination of eclipse and parhelia answers all requirements. A common sense evaluation of these facts yields: that is likely what happened.

No one in the world could yet predict eclipses in Hezekiah's day. Isaiah had no way to know of this phenomenon in advance. The setting of all the necessary conditions, as well as the timing of the events testify to a miracle God arranged in advance.

Let everyone also remember that Hezekiah was instantly healed of a fatal disease. Let us further remember that the Lord preserved Jerusalem against the world's mightiest army, which no other army had been able to stop. The shadow sign was itself a miracle, but so were these two events the sign promised. This is profoundly amazing! We experience amazement when the Bible meets the sky.

Chapter 3: An Introduction to the Astral Prophets

Part 1, Ezekiel

The Bible meets the sky in the writings of Ezekiel, and John the Elder who received the Revelation. There were others as well whose experiences involved the heavens. For instance, Zechariah (e.g., 6:1-8). John the Baptist saw the heavens opened and a dove descend upon Jesus (John 1:32-34). This is said of Jesus as well (Matthew 3:15-17; Mark 1:9-10; Luke 3:21-22 [Jesus is perhaps not the only one to see the heavens opened in Luke]). Paul's call on the Damascus Road to be a disciple of Jesus Christ starts with a breaking-in from heaven, seen in the light from heaven shining around Paul and his companions (Acts 9:3-9). It ends with the overwhelming physical toll on Paul: temporary blindness and inability to eat (Acts 9:8-9). These are characteristic of someone who has been visited from the sky. But simply in terms of the volume of material they offer us, Ezekiel and John bring us the majority of the intersections of the Word of God and the sky. We will confine this brief introduction to them without commenting on the entirety of their works.

Prophets are often thought of in terms of their oracles and their visions. Sometimes their work also involved messages that were enacted in public, such as when Jeremiah publicly smashed a clay flask to illustrate his warning of the nation's coming destruction (Jeremiah 19). Jeremiah is an example of how one prophet's work could include oracles, visions, and enacted messages, all in obedience to revelation. Astral prophecy (i.e., connected with the stars and their realm) is seen much less in the Bible than these other forms; the astral prophets are less recognized as deliverers of a further kind of prophecy. Understanding that the sky is the canvas on which their works are painted contributes to understanding what those prophecies actually mean.

Astral prophecy is a little-recognized dimension of prophecy. For that reason we include this introduction. Astral prophecy comprises one of the intersections of Bible and sky.

Ezekiel the Priest

One of the most fascinating personalities in the entire Bible is Ezekiel the son of Buzi. The cataclysmic events that he witnessed, endured, and suffered as an obedient prophet of the Lord are not as well-known as they deserve to be. Part of the reason is that interpreters too often jump to his oracles, and especially his visions, in an attempt to predict the future—the end of the world. They misrepresent the book and the man behind the book.

Here is a brief review of the life of Ezekiel prior to his prophetic call. He was born two or three years before the immensely important discovery of the Scroll of the Law in the temple. Ezekiel's father was a priest; we are not told if he was a priest faithful to the Lord, or one of the many syncretistic priests who mixed Canaanite religions with the worship practices of Israel. The leadership of the nation had gone through years of violating their covenant with the Lord, and the Law the covenant was based upon. Many no longer knew there had even been such a covenant. For too many years the gods of the Canaanites were honored and served throughout the land, where the Lord only was to be worshiped. Altars and sacred poles were everywhere.

The Canaanite religions were not about righteousness and justice. They focused on various forms of the god Baal, a god of nature and weather. Israel had come to share the Canaanite belief that appeasing Baal was necessary for a successful harvest, and that required cult prostitution as a way of starting nature's cycles. This of course resulted in the transmission of diseases, and the dishonoring of the family, but such things were not of concern to the Canaanites, who also killed some of their own children in sacrifice to their gods.

With the discovery of the Scroll of the Law a thorough reform would sweep the land under the new King, Josiah, who began to rule at the age of eight. Clearly, he had advisors in those early years of his reign who were still among the faithful to the Lord. In just a few years after his accession to the throne Josiah's reform had begun. The prophetess Huldah was asked about this reform, because Judah already stood guilty of generations of disobedience. The Law said such disobedience would be met with punishment. Huldah said that in view of Josiah's desire to set things right, the Lord would send Judah's deserved punishment later, but that it would come.

What a time for a young priest like Ezekiel to be alive! Surely now the immediate future might be bright. Blessings could come to Judah if the Lord would forgive their sins. The disaster that had befallen Israel to the north might not be visited now on Judah until someday far off. Israel was gone; Judah would endure. Faithful priests were important again. Evil was going to be replaced by good.

Then a tragedy occurred in Judah that must have been experienced by its citizens as the assassinations of John F. Kennedy, Martin Luther King, Jr., and Robert Kennedy were in the United States in the Twentieth Century. Josiah was killed in battle by Egyptian forces at Megiddo in 609. The transformative son of David and servant of God was suddenly and violently gone. Hope left with him. The evil influences of earlier years returned without resistance. Jehoahaz, Joshiah's youngest son, ruled for just three months before Pharaoh Necho replaced him with his older brother, Jehoiachim.

Ezekiel saw all this. He was not yet thirty years old when King Josiah died. The foreboding words of Huldah's prophecy about destruction yet-to-come could not be forgotten. Would Egypt remain the dominant superpower? Would Babylon overtake Assyria? What would the future hold for God's people? Pundits and professional prophets offered their theories, most of them hopeful about tomorrow. But with the return of idolatry and its concomitant murders, adulteries, and injustice, the Lord called and sent genuine prophets to warn this nation that its sins were grave. Without repentance, Judah would go the way of Israel. Chief among those prophets was Jeremiah. Young Ezekiel probably saw and heard Jeremiah as he lived out the difficult life of one called to be God's messenger of dire news.

Babylon's Nebuchadnezzar besieged Jerusalem. Jehoiachim refused to pay him tribute. The siege failed. A second attempt to besiege and conquer Jerusalem succeeded with the death of Jehoiachim, and the accession of his son, Jehoiachin. In 597/596 B.C., a deportation of Jehoiachin and the leading citizens of Judah brought them into the Kingdom of Babylon to be resettled there. The strategy behind this was to remove all leadership from the homeland, while adding skilled and intelligent people to Babylonia. Ezekiel was among those deported. In an event that must have resembled the Trail of Tears experience of the Native Americans, citizens of Judah walked or rode the hundreds of miles to the east that brought them into Babylonia.

Some of them were forced to live and work by the Chebar canal. It was a waterway between the Tigris and Euphrates Rivers. There Ezekiel, who had already seen so much of the turbulent things of this world, was summoned to visions of the sky.

> *In the thirtieth year, in the fourth month, on the fifth day of the month, as I was among the exiles by the Chebar canal, the heavens were opened, and I saw visions of God. On the fifth day of the month (it was the fifth year of the exile of King Jehoiachin), the word of the LORD came to Ezekiel the priest, the son of Buzi, in the land of the Chaldeans by the Chebar canal, and the hand of the LORD was upon him there.*
>
> Ezekiel 1:1-3

As our investigation of Ezekiel's prophetic call begins, let us all realize that we are now changing our perspective. We have been encountering the heavens as we followed the experiences of Joshua, David, and Hezekiah. But now we will be seeing them a different way through the experience of Ezekiel. The stopping sun, the drawn sword of the angel over Araunah's threshing floor, and the moving of the sun's shadow on the ma'aloth of Ahaz all involved the things of the sky, but each of them could be seen by any observer.

What Ezekiel saw was starkly different. The prophet was shown the heavens as others were not permitted to see them. This perspective cannot be attained, it must be granted. We can only hear and attempt to imagine what Ezekiel saw. Our perspective is now a spiritual and visionary one, an alternate state of consciousness perspective shared with us in words. As we read of other individuals from other times and in other religions, when an individual enters an alternate state of consciousness the experience can be absolutely devastating. These are Ezekiel's words following his encounter with the Lord when Ezekiel was summoned to be a prophet:

> *"...and I came to the exiles at Tel-abib, who were dwelling by the Chebar canal, and I sat where they were dwelling. And I sat there overwhelmed among them seven days."* *Ezekiel 3:15*

Rabbis later referred to the throne of God in Ezekiel's vision as the Merkava, the Chariot. It was synonymous with God's presence. They realized that receiving a vision like Ezekiel's poses danger to the seer. After all, "no one can see God and live" (Exodus 33:18-23). They related the following about Pardes, which means the Orchard, the experience of the presence of God.

> *"Our Rabbis have taught, four entered into the Pardes. They were Ben Azai, Ben Zoma, Aher, and Rabbi Akiba. Ben Azai gazed and died. Of him it is written, "precious in the eyes of HaShem is the death of his pious ones" (Tehilim 116, 15). Ben Zoma gazed, and went insane. Of him, it is written, "have you found honey, eat your share lest you become full,*

and vomit it up." (Mishlei 25, 16). Aher became an apostate. Rabbi Akiba entered, and exited in peace."

Hagigah 14B

We think of holiness in terms of moral and ethical purity. That is only one dimension of "the holy." Holiness is otherness of an overwhelming intensity... Rudolf Otto called it the non-rational dimension of religion (note, non-rational, not irrational). An encounter with the holy transforms the person who receives it.

What Ezekiel saw in his vision was a succession of symbols. Modern readers often do not realize that these symbols come from the sky. Theories about Ezekiel cover a wide range. In 1968 Erich Von Däniken reaped financial rewards for his best-selling book, *Chariots of the Gods*. He said Ezekiel's vision, which we are about to investigate, was really an alien spacecraft. The part about the "wheels within the wheels" was especially open to such speculation for those who do not know the true context. Others have seen in Ezekiel a man suffering from epilepsy, or a man with a psychiatric disorder. Of course, to reach conclusions such as these one must be either unaware of the profound meaning in this prophetic book, or unwilling to acknowledge it. These words are not the result of one who was of unsound mind, but one who communicated a message with such effectiveness that his words and actions have not yet been forgotten. His call to be God's prophet involved doing strange things, such as not speaking for a time, making a miniature Jerusalem on a brick, and not mourning when his wife died. But when one understands that there was an enacted type of prophecy in addition to oracles, Ezekiel can be heard in his proper context. This is the context of prophecy. It includes a familiarity with the sky.

> [4] *As I looked, behold, a stormy wind came out of the north, and a great cloud, with brightness around it, and fire flashing forth continually, and in the midst of the fire, as it were gleaming metal.* [5] *And from the midst of it came the likeness of four living creatures. And this was their appearance: they had a human likeness,* [6] *but each had four faces, and each of them had four wings.* [7] *Their legs were straight,*

and the soles of their feet were like the sole of a calf's foot. And they sparkled like burnished bronze. [8] *Under their wings on their four sides they had human hands. And the four had their faces and their wings thus:* [9] *their wings touched one another. Each one of them went straight forward, without turning as they went.*[10] *As for the likeness of their faces, each had a human face. The four had the face of a lion on the right side, the four had the face of an ox on the left side, and the four had the face of an eagle.*

Ezekiel 1:4-10

A stormy wind, a cloud, flashing fire (lightning?)—these all say to us: weather. As we have seen, weather is part of the sky. There was no concept of an atmosphere with space above it. All that was high above the ground constituted the heavens. So the approaching spectacle for Ezekiel is already shown to be from the sky in the first verse.

The four living creatures would have brought to mind the four cardinal constellations as they were known in Ezekiel's day. This is extremely important, because Babylon was the center of Chaldean star worship. The Babylonians claimed knowledge of the heavens, and the favor of the gods in the heavens. They surely insulted the exiles with reminders that Babylon's sky gods had been victorious over them and their God. This is attested by the opening of Psalm 137:

By the waters of Babylon,
there we sat down and wept,
when we remembered Zion.
[2] *On the willows there*
we hung up our lyres.
[3] *For there our captors*
required of us songs,
and our tormentors, mirth, saying,
"Sing us one of the songs of Zion!"

In Ezekiel's vision the four constellation-faced-beings are servants of Yahweh, and Yahweh alone. They are not his equals, they only accompany his throne. Yahweh is Lord of all the heavens with all their various, identified beings.

In 1914 Franz Boll made the following identifications of the living creatures' faces with Babylonian constellations. It is important to understand that these constellations are ninety degrees apart in the sky, so that they are evenly placed with respect to each other. They are the constellations of the seasons, and each holds a bright star. This is the way in which the four living creatures surround the throne, although they are beneath it. They therefore represent the entire sky, the whole expanse of the heavens.

The face of a man
This face probably refers to the Babylonian constellation, Scorpion-man. The constellation we have come to know as Scorpio had a human face in Babylonian sky lore. The Gilgamesh Epic tells of scorpion people who are with the Scorpion-man, who guards the western gate of the sun. Remember that this constellation is 90 degrees from its neighbors to the East and West. These are Leo, and Aquarius which was then the Babylonian Thunderbird. At 180 degrees is Taurus.

The face of a lion
This corresponds to Leo, still the Lion today as it was in ancient Mesopotamia and Arabia, and all through Western astrology as well.

The face of an ox
The ox corresponds to Taurus, the bull constellation. Notice that in 9:3; 10:1; 10:2; and 10:3 the reference is to a cherub. That calls to mind a body which is consistent with the form of an ox.

The face of an eagle
Pegasus is a winged horse to us, but like Scorpio, it has evolved. It was once a thunderbird figure in Babylonian sky lore. (Thorkild Jacobsen, *The Treasures of Darkness: A History of Mesopotamian*

Religion, Yale University Press, 1976, pp. 128-129). So, the face of an eagle corresponds to that thunderbird constellation.

> *Now as I looked at the living creatures, I saw a wheel on the earth beside the living creatures, one for each of the four of them. As for the appearance of the wheels and their construction: their appearance was like the gleaming of beryl. And the four had the same likeness, their appearance and construction being as it were a wheel within a wheel. When they went, they went in any of their four directions without turning as they went. And their rims were tall and awesome, and the rims of all four were full of eyes all around.* Ezekiel 1:15-18

Wheels within Wheels

The wheels that suddenly appeared by the four living creatures signify mobility. Certainly God will not be limited to any one place. This is not the God of any single locality or region. That is the point.

Figure 23. This drawing presents one **way to understand the "whirling wheels", wheels within wheels, in** Ezekiel's vision. The rims are at 90 degrees to one another. Author: RootOfAllLIght. Creative Commons Attribution-Share Alike 4.0 International.

It is challenging to understand what Ezekiel means by "wheel within a wheel". One option is that we are to think of the wheels as perpendicular to one another. How axles were to figure into this lies completely outside the vision; these wheels needed no axles. They could roll forward and backward, or from side to side, without turning as the front wheels of a car would pivot with the turning of the steering wheel. These wheels were unlimited as to where they could go. They "darted" as they went, meaning that their movement was swift, without apparent acceleration or deceleration.

A second way of envisioning what is meant by wheels within wheels is the parhelia we have already discussed in connection with the shadow's retreat as a sign for King Hezekiah. In fact, parhelia that are especially vivid sometimes take the form of bright circles intersecting other bright circles. This connects us with the sky again. The wheels within wheels bring to mind the parhelic circles, and the color of those circles matches Ezekiel's description of their color: like beryl.

Eyes

Each wheel has a rim filled with eyes. Trying to imagine such a sight leads to a truly strange mental picture. Maybe that is part of the the intent. But eyes was an expression sometimes used of stars. (When we look ahead at 10:12 we find that the wheels had spokes which were also filled with eyes.) If stars is what the term eyes means here, the eyes tell us that these wheels belong to the heavenly realm. They provide the mobility for the throne of God. In the vision, that throne is about to move, and this is central to the message of the vision, as we will see.

Figure 24. Here is an example of a wheel within a wheel as found in the sky over Thailand on September 11, 2021. There was no rain or fog; the parhelion lasted about five minutes. By Peterbainbridge - Own work, CC BY-SA 3.0, https://commons.wikimedia.org/w/index.php?curid=21250404.

> *[22] Over the heads of the living creatures there was the likeness of an expanse, shining like awe-inspiring crystal, spread out above their heads. [23] And under the expanse their wings were stretched out straight, one toward another. And each creature had two wings covering its body. [24] And when they went, I heard the sound of their wings like the sound of many waters, like the sound of the Almighty, a sound of tumult like the sound of an army. When they stood still, they let down their wings. [25] And there came a voice from above the expanse over their heads. When they stood still, they let down their wings. [26] And above the expanse over their heads there was the likeness of a*

throne, in appearance like sapphire; and seated above the likeness of a throne was a likeness with a human appearance. Ezekiel 1:22-27

The Awe-inspiring Crystal Expanse

Figure 25. Milky way on Pietrasecca by Camillo Granchelli, CC BY-SA 4.0 <https://creativecommons.org/licenses/by-sa/4.0>, via Wikimedia Commons

The expanse above the four living creatures makes us think of the Milky Way, which on a clear night does appear to be just what Ezekiel describes as a crystal expanse. We will meet this expanse and the four living creatures beneath it again when we discuss the Revelation.

The Likeness of a Sapphire Throne

It should not surprise anyone that Yahweh would appear upon a throne in Ezekiel's vision. He is the Lord and King of all the heavenly host. In the sky is at least one constellation that has been understood to include a throne. It is Cassiopeia, in the northern sky. The constellation is comprised of five stars. It has the shape of the letter W which traces the form of the chair on which Cassiopeia is seated.

Sapphire is a deep blue color, the color of the sky near the Milky Way. This would be the appropriate color for the background sky around the throne.

The Return of the Vision

The text of Ezekiel goes on from this vision of the Glory of the Lord with five intervening chapters before we hear again of the living creatures, the wheels, and the throne. The intervening chapters elaborate for us the reason for Ezekiel's call: the profound sin of the nation that is leading to destruction unless repentance comes quickly.

Here are some of those behaviors on Ezekiel's part which some have found so bizarre, yet make complete sense in their context. Again, this behavior got attention then, and does so to this day. Briefly put:

- Ezekiel is commanded to engrave Jerusalem on a brick. He is to build a wall around it, with camps of soldiers around it, and a siege ramp next to it. He is to lie on his left side near the brick for 390 days, and then on his right.
- Ezekiel is commanded to take a sharp sword, shave the hair of his head and beard with it as though it were a razor, and then divide the hair into three parts. One part is to be burned in the city, another part is to be struck with the

sword around Jerusalem, and the third part is to be thrown to the wind.
- Ezekiel was commanded to dig into the wall, having been taken in the Spirit from Babylon to Jerusalem. As he dug, he opened a hidden entrance and saw a number of abominable actions of the people there.

The text accompanying these behaviors explains their meaning in the context of Judah's impending demise.

Then, with chapters nine and ten, the vision of the throne returns. Yahweh is now leaving his temple that had been his dwelling since the days of Solomon. The cherubim rise up from the earth. The throne is last seen over the east gate of the temple. Yahweh has determined that this place is no longer acceptable for his dwelling.

What Does it Mean?

Ezekiel's overwhelming call to speak for Yahweh happens within a vision of Yahweh's throne. The setting is cosmic, not local. The hosts of heaven are represented by the four living creatures. The sovereign freedom of Yahweh to be any place is immediately clear. His choice had been to "make his name dwell" in Jerusalem at the temple built there by Solomon long ago. (See Solomon's prayer, 1 Kings 8:22-53). This will no longer be the case. The throne of the Lord is seen by the prophet as it rises and leaves, now to go to the East. Would the Glory of the Lord ever return to the temple?

Despite what the captors will say, Yahweh has not been defeated in the city of his choice by the gods of the sky-worshiping Babylonians. In Ezekiel's vision all the gods of the Babylonians are conspicuously missing from the sky. Anu, Marduk, Enlil, and Tiamat are nowhere to be seen. It is the righteousness of Yahweh alone that has caused him to move from the midst of this sinful people and their temple.

At the end of the book is Ezekiel's lengthy vision of a new temple. It is important to notice that in Revelation there is no temple in the new Jerusalem descending from heaven, because of the presence of the Lamb. But in Ezekiel's vision of the future temple, the Glory of the Lord is seen again in that Temple.

> [1] *Then he led me to the gate, the gate facing east.* [2] *And behold, the glory of the God of Israel was coming from the east. And the sound of his coming was like the sound of many waters, and the earth shone with his glory.* [3] *And the vision I saw was just like the vision that I had seen when he came to destroy the city, and just like the vision that I had seen by the Chebar canal. And I fell on my face.* [4] *As the glory of the LORD entered the temple by the gate facing east,* [5] *the Spirit lifted me up and brought me into the inner court; and behold, the glory of the LORD filled the temple.* Ezekiel 43:1-5

Part 2, John the Elder

The other astral prophet whose visions we will discuss here briefly is John the Elder, the writer of the Revelation. Few New Testament scholars have pursued the astral dimension of Revelation to the extent I believe best. One of them was Professor Bruce Malina of Creighton University in Omaha, Nebraska. His book, *On the Genre and Message of Revelation* (Hendrickson Publishers, 1995) makes a strong and detailed case that Revelation is just what it claims to be, the vision(s) of a prophet whose experience took place above the sky. Professor Malina believed the time frame for the persons and events reflected in Revelation did not necessarily extend beyond the destruction of Jerusalem in 70 A.D. Professor Bruce Metzger and many others have understood that time frame to be slightly later—a time of persecution of Christians in Rome. For Professor Malina the city whose smoke goes up forever is Jerusalem. For Professor Metzger the city is Rome.

It may not finally be necessary to decide strictly between one viewpoint and the other. The actual ability of the prophet to announce future events within his visions means that, for instance, the mysterious, evil person whose name tallies to 666 might still have been off in the future for the people who were now about to behold the fall of Jerusalem and its temple.

Who was John?

Early church tradition has for the most part said John the Elder was the same John who accompanied Jesus as one of the Twelve. He wrote the Gospel of John. This was John, son of Zebedee, whose brother was James. A separate question is whether the John of Revelation is the same John who wrote the three letters of John in the New Testament. The nature of the Greek used in the Gospel compared to the Greek in Revelation has caused many modern scholars to say that two different people wrote these documents. Behind this conclusion is a most relevant question that must be asked and answered. Did John really experience a vision in which he was directed to write what he had seen and heard? Or is the Revelation "ninety percent perspiration and ten percent inspiration"? Those who adopt the second outlook have already rejected John's claim. They see John as a person who developed a literary work of his own, based on the apocalyptic literary forms that had been current for two centuries. John studied and used Ezekiel, Daniel, and possibly other works. In this view John was in charge of every phrase and every thought from beginning to end. Therefore, his Greek tells us that he cannot be the same John as the author of the Gospel. But if John really experienced his vision(s) "in the Spirit" and did not craft the text himself, we can understand why that Greek might be different from his usual means of writing. He was writing as he was told to write by Jesus and his angels, not as John might otherwise write as Jesus' disciple.

Today, opinion is divided on whether John of Revelation is in fact to be identified as the son of Zebedee. Another person named John who was also a witness to much of Jesus' ministry has been proposed. The prophet who gave us the Revelation tells us that he was on the Island of Patmos when the vision(s) came to him. He was banished by the Roman government because of his faith and stature as a Christian. This suggests that John was a person of importance; ordinary persons would likely have been treated more harshly, or killed. A statement from Polycrates, Bishop of Ephesus in the Second Century, says John was a priest who "wore the petalon". This was one of the emblems of the High Priest of Israel, and it was not worn every day, but only when his duties called for it. In my book *The Mystery of the Beloved Disciple* I have linked this man John to a family (Boethus) that produced several of the High Priests. It may be that John was a Sagan, a stand-in for the High Priest in case he should become unable to serve. In that case it is surely conceivable that at one time or another this John wore the petalon, even if only briefly to be certain that it would fit him if the need should arise for him to wear it as the replacement High Priest.

This matters because someone from a prominent family of priests, a member of the Jerusalem aristocracy, might more likely have been banished, rather than imprisoned or killed. We know very little about John, whether he was in fact the son of Zebedee, a fisherman from Galilee with a family business, a member of a prominent priestly family, or someone altogether different. His banishment to Patmos does suggest that he was an important priest.

The Sky in Revelation

In contrast to Ezekiel who sees the throne of God in sky terms, but does not remain in astral prophesy, the Revelation is cast in sky terms from beginning to end. Even the messages to the seven churches of Asia Minor have their sky connections. So what could be the logic behind all this?

First, as Metzger says, we must concern ourselves with what the images mean, not the images themselves. This Revelation must be interpreted. We are forced by the sky imagery to go beyond the imagery itself in the pursuit of its meaning. Some have made the mistake of failing to do this.

Second, the images have a power and a fascination that has kept Revelation alive for two thousand years. That speaks to the value of the form the Revelation takes.

Third, for Christians under persecution any documents critical of the government would be dangerous to possess. The cryptic nature of the sky images was to some extent protective.

Fourth, in Shakespeare's play, "As You Like It", Jaques says: "All the world's a stage, and all the men and women merely players;" (Act 2, scene 7). The same can be said of the sky. The people of ancient times looked up to behold a stage already filled with characters, props, and sets. These were all present to be used by God in the multiple-scene drama called the Revelation. Along with this idea comes a related one. Simply seeing the sky would bring messages from the Revelation to mind for the faithful.

If what we are saying here is true, the images of the Revelation were much less mysterious for the original audience than for us. Those people were much more familiar with the sky. So, they were more able to see through to the meanings of the symbols.

Now, let's look at just some of those symbols with the eyes of a First Century Christian living under the reality of persecution by the government of the world. Much of this has been brought to our attention by Professor Malina, but it soon becomes easy to make connections in some cases without help. We will take soundings at places in the Revelation to see if we remain in territory where referents in the vision correspond to things found in the sky.

As the Revelation begins John relates how this prophecy came about. He was on the Island of Patmos. On the Lord's day he was "in the Spirit". Hearing a voice ringing like a trumpet, John turned. He saw lampstands, and a "son of man" standing among them. Son of man is an expression which can mean (a) individual, (b) human being, (c) the Son of Man in Daniel chapter 7, with its derivative versions as in 1 Enoch. Jesus used this expression of himself. Some heard it to mean individual; others heard it as a claim to be the Son of Man who would be given dominion over the whole world. Clearly in the vision, the son of man is the exalted Jesus, speaking from Heaven. Jesus' appearance brings to mind the vision of Yahweh's throne from Ezekiel. There is a brightness, a loudness. From his mouth is seen a two-edged sword. This last part of Jesus' description takes us into the realm of symbolism already; we are not to think of the risen Jesus as actually having a sword in his mouth. Rather, this sword—two-edged—has an ability to enter a person's spirit. This sword is also powerful as a means of enforcing Jesus' will. Revelation is not the only place we find such sword imagery. " For the word of God is living and active, sharper than any two-edged sword, piercing to the division of soul and of spirit, of joints and of marrow, and discerning the thoughts and intentions of the heart." (Hebrews 4:12) We have seen an instance of a sight in the night sky which David interpreted as the sword of an angel. If we are searching for a sky image that would bring to mind a sword, it would be a comet. This does not necessarily mean that John envisioned a comet issuing from Jesus' mouth, making of it a sword. Precisely what John saw we cannot know. But the properties for the drama on the stage of the sky were present and available to be used within the vision.

Lampstands

The exalted Jesus is seen standing among seven lampstands. A lampstand was just what we would think, a stand to hold oil lamps so that their light might shine throughout a room. The meaning of the lampstands is given in 1:20. They represent the seven churches of Asia Minor to which the Revelation is primarily addressed. Can we find a counterpart to these lampstands in the sky? Most of us have seen them. They are the seven stars which form the Big Dipper, a constellation the ancient Mesopotamians called the Wagon.

Seven stars

Seven stars in the right hand of Jesus symbolize the angels in charge of the seven churches. Are these earthly angels, meaning leaders? Or are these actual spirits who watch over the believers in the churches? This is an important question. Near the Big Dipper is another constellation which we call the Little Dipper. It has seven stars.

Open door

John tells us that he was taken up through an open door in heaven. This is extremely revealing. It confirms that we are encountering astral prophecy. What John will see in the visions that follow is going to be near him, or even beneath him. He will be looking at the symbolic objects and symbolic beings of the sky from up there where they are. His vision is a kind of close-up look at what will take place in the cosmic realms. Malina shows us that an opening through the sky was thought by ancient people to exist in the North.

Throne

We saw that Cassiopeia was a likely counterpart to the throne in Ezekiel. That continues to be true for the Revelation. Further, the seven lampstands and the seven stars, the Big and Little Dippers, are in the northern sky near the throne.

Four living creatures/eyes

The four living creatures we meet surrounding the throne of God remind us immediately of the four creatures we met in Ezekiel. They are different, yet similar. Surely the vision is meant to suggest the same reality found in Ezekiel, the presence of God. But in the Revelation we are not led to think that John the Elder is the new Ezekiel. That is not the point. Enough differences exist between Ezekiel's and John's visions that we are required to think and search for the intended meanings of both.

24 Elders

As we saw in chapter 1, The Sky, some civilizations used a system of 24 decans, and others used 36. Decans were marker stars that divided the sky into parts. The 24 Elders that surround the throne of God in Revelation correspond to 24 decans that surround the sky. As for who the Elders are, they might be the twelve patriarchs of Israel and the twelve Apostles of Jesus.

Crystal sea

We saw already that an image of a crystal sea was part of Ezekiel's vision of the throne of the Lord. The Milky Way seems the perfect counterpart in the night sky as we see it. It appears clear, yet radiant literally from one end of the heavens to the other.

Lion

Jesus is identified as the Lion of the Tribe of Judah (5:5). The lion was the symbol of the tribe of Judah in the Old Testament. The point of 5:5 is that this Lion has conquered. He has strength like the lion. Jesus is also called the root and descendent of David here, and David was a conqueror. We will explore whether Magi would likely have considered events happening in Leo as pertaining to Judah, and why the answer to that is probably no. But Leo, the Lion, is a major constellation and a zodiacal house. Within this vision the correlation of the Lion of the Tribe of Judah with Leo is hard to deny.

Lamb

Then the image correlating to Jesus changes. Now it is a lamb. A lamb and a ram are not identical in meaning, but they are related. They overlap. We need not search long for a lamb. It is Aries, the ram. Those who did apply astrology to Israel saw Aries as the house and constellation of Israel. It was the first constellation to appear in the Spring. (Earlier it had been the Lion, but precession altered that over time.)

The Lamb appears to John as one that had been slain. Of course, this immediately makes Christians think of Jesus as the "Lamb of God who takes away the sin of the world" (John 1:29). The Passover lamb was slaughtered on the Eve of Passover, and its blood became a peace offering. In contrast to the Lion who is the symbol of strength, the Lamb is the symbol of weakness, yet it will be the Lamb as a Lamb who alone will be able to break the seven seals, making the future events unfold. Malina (p. 111) brings us a most interesting point about this lamb. The head of the constellation Aries is turned back over its shoulder, which could be taken as a broken neck. We have examples within the history of the church of art depicting the Lamb of God. These depictions often show the Lamb with his head turned back over its shoulder, just like the constellation. This corresponds with how Aries was construed in the sky. If we think of the Lamb's neck as broken, Aries immediately correlates with the Lamb "standing as though slain." (5:6).

Figure 26. **Left**, Aries as drawn by Sidney Hall (1788-1831) Public domain, via Wikimedia Commons . **Right**, an example of the Lamb of God in church art from St. Aloysius Catholic Church in Shandon, Ohio. Nheyob, CC BY-SA 3.0 <https://creativecommons.org/licenses/by-sa/3.0>, via Wikimedia Commons In each case the head is turned back over the shoulder. One could interpret this as a broken neck, and therefore the lamb appears "as though slain". Notice the seven seals on the book in the stained glass window. See Revelation 5:1-2.

The Dragon

> *And another sign appeared in heaven: behold, a great red dragon, with seven heads and ten horns, and on his heads seven diadems. [4] His tail swept down a third of the stars of heaven and cast them to the earth. And the dragon stood before the woman who was about to give birth, so that when she bore her child he might devour it. [5] She gave birth to a male child, one who is to rule all the nations with a rod of iron, but her child was caught up to God and to his throne, [6] and the woman fled into the wilderness, where she has a place prepared by God, in which she is to be nourished for 1,260 days.*
>
> Revelation 12:3-6

The Woman in the vision will be discussed at greater length in Chapter 4. She has her sky counterpart in the constellation Virgo. Now we turn our attention to the Dragon. It appears in heaven near the woman. It attempts to devour the child fails as the child is taken beyond his reach. Its tail sweeps down a third of the stars within John's vision. This can only mean that the Dragon has awesome strength. It is red. Colors were important to ancient astrologers, and their systems of what colors mean are complex, and beyond the scope of this investigation. We will say only this about the color of the Dragon here: red sometimes represents the South.

For many scholars today the seven heads represent the seven hills on which the city of Rome was built. The horns represent strength, and ten of them correlate to ten emperors that have already come.

Near the woman in the sky is Hydra, a constellation usually depicted as a very large serpent. How does a serpent become a dragon? The answer may lie in Isaiah 27:1: "In that day the LORD with his hard and great and strong sword will punish Leviathan the fleeing serpent, Leviathan the twisting serpent, and he will slay the dragon that is in the sea." The parallelism of Hebrew poetry finds little or no difference between a twisting serpent and a dragon in the sea. Others scholars have more to say about why Hydra should be thought of as the Dragon, or an earlier constellation where Hydra is now, comprising the present Scorpio and Libra. Still others look to another constellation, Draco.

Hydra was already a monster in Greek mythology with multiple heads. Hercules was given the task of killing it. When one head was cut off, two others would grow. This is an example of the kind of sky background that accompanies the vision; these images were already to be found throughout the popular cultures. That actor on the stage of the sky which was Hydra now played the new role of the Dragon in John's vision. As for the horns, some depictions of Hydra include horns on its heads.

One of the strong reasons to understand Hydra to be the Dragon is the fact that the sky is relatively dark near Hydra. That corresponds to the vision, that one third of the stars of the sky were swept down by the Dragon's tail. Some believe that annual meteor showers coming from this part of the sky are what is meant by the reference to the swept-down stars.

The Woman is taken to the wilderness where she is to be nourished for 1260 days. Readers of Daniel will recognize 1260 days as "a time, two times, and half a time", three and one half years. Because this amount of time and its variants (1290, 1335) were already associated with the past when Antiochus Epiphanes persecuted God's people violently in an attempt to eradicate Judaism from the world (Daniel 7:25, 12:7), 1260 days became in Revelation the symbolic designation for a period of extreme persecution, with a beginning, but also an end.

What is the wilderness? Again, the answer may have multiple parts. The recurring plot line of the story of God's people had Israel in the wilderness, fed and clothed by Yahweh for forty years. The Jewish Diaspora corresponded to God's people in a different kind of wilderness. The believers in Jesus who fled from Jerusalem when they saw its destruction coming went to Pella (Eusebius, *Church History*, 3,5,3). In astrological terms planets had secret places (Eastern system) and exaltations (Western system). Perhaps this is the sky's counterpart to the wilderness.

Trumpets, bowls, horses

As we continue to take our soundings in the Revelation to test how often sky images might be found, we come upon trumpets, bowls of wrath, and the "four horsemen of the apocalypse". We learn from Malina that trumpets, bowls, and horses were all names for types of comets to people of the ancient world (*On the Genre and Meaning of Revelation*). There were other types of comets as well. He provides numerous examples. Again we find counterparts to the images in the vision, and we find them in the sky.

The beast/666

Probably the most intriguing single symbol of the entire Revelation is found in chapter 13, at least as far as popular interest is concerned. There a beast is described who follows a first beast.

> [11] *Then I saw another beast rising out of the earth. It had two horns like a lamb and it spoke like a dragon.* [12] *It exercises all the authority of the first beast in its presence and makes the earth and its inhabitants worship the first beast, whose mortal wound was healed.* [13] *It performs great signs, even making fire come down from heaven to earth in front of people,* [14] *and by the signs that it is allowed to work in the presence of the beast it deceives those who dwell on earth, telling them to make an image for the beast that was wounded by the sword and yet lived.* [15] *And it was allowed to give breath to the image of the beast, so that the image of the beast might even speak and might cause those who would not worship the image of the beast to be slain.* [16] *Also it causes all, both small and great, both rich and poor, both free and slave to be marked on the right hand or the forehead,* [17] *so that no one can buy or sell unless he has the mark, that is, the name of the beast or the number of its name.* [18] *This calls for wisdom: let the one who has understanding calculate the number of the beast, for it is the number of a man, and his number is 666.* Revelation 13:11-18

Many features of this part of the vision deserve more comment than we will give here. But let us be aware of at least the following:

- The beast rose from the earth, not from heaven.
- The horns are a symbol of power.
- The Dragon is Satan, so speaking like the Dragon is to speak as Satan's mouthpiece.

- The mortal wound associated with the first beast has been thought by many to refer to a legend that Emperor Nero, a persecutor of Christians during whose time of rule both Peter and Paul were put to death in Rome, had been raised from the dead.
- Making an image for someone is the same as worshiping that person. Emperor worship actually began with Augustus, who made the claim that a comet represented the deification of Julius Caesar after his assassination. By the time of Tiberius, during the ministry of Jesus, coins used the term "divi" in relationship to the Emperor, a claim to divinity. With some thirty more years the idea was entrenched. Nero was to be worshiped as a god.
- Fire coming down from heaven is difficult to match to any known happening in ancient times, but first we must recognize that the fire comes down *from heaven*. We are still in the territory of the sky. It is noteworthy that the shields of Legion XII, Fulminata, were painted with crossed lightning bolts. From this legion came a new Emperor, Vespasian. With Vespasian, persecution by Nero temporarily subsided, but it resumed with Domitian. Perhaps it is the awesome military power of Caesar in the service of evil that is meant here by fire called down from heaven, represented by the lightning bolt.
- An economic boycott of believers in Jesus appears to be in place, so that no one can subsist who does not worship the beast. That is the significance of the "mark of the beast".
- The number of the beast is the number of a man. This is a most important direction for all who would interpret the vision. The entity behind this symbol of the beast is a human being. His name, coded in numbers, is 666.

Roman numerals are more familiar to us than the Jewish system. But the ideas behind the systems are the same. Numbers are represented by letters which are added or subtracted from each other. Although the Revelation is written in Greek, the context requires us to be open to the idea that Aramaic or Hebrew letters are being used here. So who can this beast be, and can he be found in the sky, consistent with what we have seen so far?

Nero Caesar was written in Aramaic letters as RSC NOREN (NERON CSR from left to right). The N at the end of NERON is sometimes dropped. The sum of these letters in the full name is 666. If the N is dropped, the total becomes 616, and some ancient manuscripts read 616 instead of 666. That is a strong indication that from earliest times Christians understood the beast to be Nero.

Certainly, beasts are to be found in the sky. But Professor Malina makes this observation which speaks to the nature of the Revelation. We must think of numbers now in another way. Ancient philosophers like Pythagoras thought about numbers, and some even thought numbers were at the metaphysical foundation of all that is. In their consideration of numbers, they noticed what we call square numbers. We use this concept yet today. For instance, 5 squared is 25. The square results from a number multiplied by itself. And if a chart is made of rows of five points, the chart will indeed take the shape of a square.

We are not familiar with triangular numbers. These are numbers that make a particular series. The triangular number is the sum of points making equilateral triangles. The series begins with 1 which is considered a triangle in itself. The next simplest triangle has three points, so adding the points gives three. The next triangle will have three points per side; it gives the number 6. So the triangular numbers starting with 1 are 3, 6, 10, 15, 21 and so on.

666 is a triangular number. In the sky is the constellation known as Triangulum, a simple triangle as its name implies. So, besides any beasts we may wish to find in the heavens to correspond to the beasts in the vision, there is even a 666.

What does it all mean?

John's vision concerns cosmic powers, not local ones. What better setting could there be for that vision than the cosmos, the sky? The more one learns about the constellations, the terminology, and the belief systems that went with the sky in the ancient world, the more context one has for the meaning of the vision.

In a cosmos so vast, what are seven struggling little churches in Asia Minor? But they learn that the cosmic Christ is aware of them, and has sent word to them, along with an assurance that the future is in his hands. Missing from heaven are the gods and spirits the powerful nations of the world claim as their own.

"It is up to the astral prophet to make known what he has come to learn and read in the sky, and thus reveal God's purpose to his brothers and sisters" (Malina p. 132).

The stuff the sky is made of is the same stuff the vision is made of. It must be interpreted so that its true meaning emerges for the faithful. There is no diminishing of the images in the Revelation when we learn of their connections with known objects in the sky. Quite the opposite.

If you are one of those who have the opportunity to see the sky away from city lights and pollution, look up and let the sky remind you of the vision constantly. See the seven stars of the Big Dipper and recall the seven lampstands where Jesus walked. See Leo, or Aries, or the Crystal Sea/Milky Way and recall the words of the Revelation associated with them. See Venus before sunrise, and remember Jesus' words about himself as the bright Morning Star, promise of a new day soon to arrive. The message of Revelation still speaks, and the silent stars amplify its words.

CHAPTER 4: THE STAR OF BETHLEHEM

Star of Wonder

No instance of the Bible meeting sky is better known than the star reported in the second chapter of Matthew. That story is told nowhere else in the Bible. Known as the Christmas Star, the Star of the Magi, and the Star of Bethlehem, this celestial phenomenon signaled that the King of the Jews had now been born. Magi representing other nations understood that signal, and travelled a long distance to find the King, honor him, and present him with gifts. These Magi are usually thought of as three in number, and they have acquired names over the centuries: Caspar, Melchior, and Balthasar. Not all this is biblical, however.

It has long been the practice of skeptics to disregard this account as pure legend. They point to the movement of the star, and to its coming to rest over Bethlehem. What kind of star does that? Citing other sky phenomena that accompanied the death of Julius Caesar, or of the birth of the magus Tiridates, they say the biblical story is simply what would be expected concerning a messianic king, and therefore must be an invention. The prophecy in Numbers (24:15-19) that a "star will rise from Jacob" is another reason for someone to make up such a tale, they say.

Others think of the story of the Star as an embellishment of the larger Jesus story. They consider it a developed reflection on his birth that is not really concerned with facts, but with meaning. They would call this story a kind of interpretation, sometimes known as midrash, more than an accurate report. So for them it would not stand in the way of faith in Christ if the Star itself should turn out not to be real. They are ready to set it aside.

Claims that the Star of Bethlehem has no basis in fact actually become extremely difficult to maintain when the full truth emerges. That truth is multi-faceted, taking us into the history of the time, and the phenomena in the sky, during the final days of Herod the King.

Figure 27. The Herodium. Here at this fortress Herod the Great was buried. Seetheholyland.net, CC BY-SA 2.0 <https://creativecommons.org/licenses/by-sa/2.0>, via Wikimedia Commons.

The Death of Herod, "King of the Jews"

All who begin to investigate the circumstances of the birth of Christ soon learn that one issue emerges as pivotal for determining *when* this birth happened. Both Matthew and Luke tell us that Jesus was born while Herod the Great was the ruler of Judea. His title given by the Roman Senate was King of the Jews. Jesus was born before Herod's death, but that is where the problem lies. When did Herod die? Opinion is divided on the answer to this crucial question.

The majority opinion in the 20th and 21st centuries has been that Herod's death took place in the year 4 B.C. That is based on a careful reading of Josephus' history, buttressed by "dates" on the coins of his three surviving sons. When the number of the highest regnal year to be found on a son's coin is subtracted from the year he is reported to have died, it has appeared that all three began to rule around 4 B.C.

Another group of scholars maintains that Herod died in 1 B.C. This is not really a new theory. It is quite consistent with the dating system the western world has used for many centuries. The person who developed this system was a medieval monk, Dionysius Exiguus. He may have been off the mark for the year of Jesus' birth, but perhaps not as far off as the majority opinion—i.e., Herod died in 4 B.C.—would require.

The many ancient witness of the church place the birth of Jesus in a span of time corresponding to part of 3 B.C., and part of 2 B.C. So, for a long time today's majority opinion was unheard of.

As the year of Herod's death is one key to when Jesus was born, a lunar eclipse is one of the keys to when Herod died. Josephus, who depends here on the history of Nicolas of Damascus within Herod's own court, reports of an act of insurrection led by two religious leaders, Judas, son of Saripheus. and Matthias, son of Margalothus. When they heard a false rumor that Herod was dead, the rioters stormed the temple to remove a Roman eagle image which Herod had placed there. All were arrested, and most were later released. But Herod made an example of the two leaders. The ailing monarch raised himself up on his elbow to speak, and ordered them burned alive. Josephus says that on that night there was an eclipse of the moon.

Lunar eclipses occurred over Judea in 5 B.C., 4 B.C., and 1 B.C. A few have opted for the 5 B.C. eclipse, but the two most-discussed candidates today for the lunar event preceding Herod's death are the eclipse of March 12/13, 4 B.C., and January 9/10, 1 B.C.

Josephus' Summary of Herod's Illness

In the final months of Herod's life the King was both physically and mentally ill. Flavius Josephus says this of his condition:

> *"But now Herod's distemper greatly increased upon him after a severe manner, and this by God's judgment upon him for his sins; for a fire glowed in him slowly, which did not so much appear to the touch outwardly, as it augmented his pains inwardly; for it brought upon him a vehement appetite to eating, which he could not avoid to supply with one sort of food or other. His entrails were also ex-ulcerated, and the chief violence of his pain lay on his colon; an aqueous and transparent liquor also had settled itself about his feet, and a like matter afflicted him at the bottom of his belly. Nay, further, his privy-member was putrefied, and produced worms; and when he sat upright, he had a difficulty of breathing, which was very loathsome, on account of the stench of his breath, and the quickness of its returns; he had also convulsions in all parts of his body, which increased his strength to an insufferable degree."*
>
> Josephus, Antiquities 17:6:5, Whiston translation

Dr. Jan Hirschmann, MD, participated in an "historical autopsy" of Herod based on his symptoms for the Historical Clinical Pathologic Conference (CPC). "At first, I considered Hodgkin's disease and some diseases of the liver," said Hirschmann. Chronic kidney disease covered all of Herod's symptoms except gangrene of the genitalia. Dr. Hirschmann decided that Herod's death was probably caused by chronic kidney disease complicated by Fournier's gangrene, an unusual infection affecting the male genitalia. (https://www.medicalbag.com/home/features/what-killed-em/king-herod/ May 15, 2021). Herod's decline was exceedingly painful. His physicians could neither save, nor help him. Josephus indicates that Herod was first willing to try any possible cure, but later gave up all hope of recovery.

Herod the Great was not descended from the royal Hasmonean family. In fact, his ancestry was of Nabatean Arabs, and his family had only converted to Judaism. So, many of his contemporaries did not consider him to be a true Jew, nor a legitimate king of Jewish people and their land. Herod endured this smoldering resentment and hatred among the people. They were of the same opinion as Josephus, that Herod's misery had been sent by God to punish Herod for his sins.

Herod became intensely suspicious that plots were in motion to kill him and seize his throne. Such suspicion was not completely without foundation, but it contributed to an ever-increasing insecurity and fear. In a despot like Herod, irrational fear could become a very dangerous thing for many people. Herod's physical decline was matched by a mental and emotional decline. Fear, anger and revenge became his driving forces.

Within the palace suspicion had grown like a poisonous plant for some time, watered by different factions of Herod's relatives. One faction was comprised of the sons who had been born to the beloved Hasmonean Queen Miriamne. Herod had put her to death for plotting his assassination. Her sons, Alexander and Aristobulus, were determined in Herod's will to be successors to the throne. But would they be content to wait? Voices whispered in Herod's ear not to trust them, especially the voices of Herod's sister and his son Antipater, whose mother was Herod's first wife, Doris. Herod now suspected that Alexander and Aristobulus were plotting against him.

When he became convinced of their guilt on the basis of circumstantial evidence, Herod received permission from Caesar to have them tried for treason by dignitaries assembled in Beirut. Saturninus, the Governor of Syria, presided at the trial. The Hasmonean sons were convicted and executed. Any threat of an uprising to reinstate Hasmonean rule was now gone.

But Herod's relief was short-lived. He learned that his son Antipater, chief accuser of the Hasmonean brothers, had been lying. In fact, Antipater was plotting the overthrow of his father, and he had let his father destroy the Hasmonean challengers for him. Antipater was in Rome when Herod learned the truth. He summoned Antipater home, keeping his knowledge of the plot secret. Herod was driven now by his desire to see Antipater put to death. Antipater arrived and was immediately arrested, held in the palace to await his trial, to be held the following day. He was found guilty, and kept in the palace until permission to execute him should arrive from Caesar.

Herod's physical symptoms had now become almost unbearable. He momentarily succumbed to an impulse to take his own life, even with Antipater still alive. Asking for an apple and a knife as he often did, he decided to use the knife to kill himself. But a courtier stopped the king, and wailing soon sounded throughout the palace. When Antipater heard the wailing he thought Herod had died, so he offered money to the guards to release him. Learning this, Herod ordered Antipater to be killed instantly. Josephus says Herod died five days later.

Somewhere in this time as death approached, Herod ordered the leading Jews throughout the land to be sequestered in the hippodrome at Jericho. When the word went forth that Herod had died, they were to be killed. That way, Herod reasoned, there would be mourning associated with his death. The order was not carried out, though Herod had made those close to him promise to do it. Some modern historians don't believe this story has basis in fact, but Josephus reported it as true. It speaks to Herod's mental and psychological condition before his death. It should also be borne in mind when we recall the story in Matthew of Herod's order to kill all male children in and around Bethlehem under the age of two.

Sometime within this overall period of Herod's physical and psychological misery, foreign Magi came to the palace in Jerusalem asking: "Where is he who has been born King of the Jews? For we saw his star when it rose and have come to worship him." (Matthew 2:2) For Herod, what should have been the best possible news was instead the worst. Some new and unknown challenger was threatening his throne. Herod lied to the Magi about his intentions as he tried to learn more about this new king. Herod's real desire was to find him and kill him. This is as Matthew reports.

Josephus tells of another execution ordered by Herod during this period that deserves mention here. It happened shortly before the king died. When six thousand Pharisees refused an oath of allegiance to Caesar and to Herod, we are told that some among the Pharisees who were thought to have a prophetic gift predicted an end to Herod and his dynasty. A eunuch named Bagoas believed that prediction, and was told that the new king would grant him power to have children of his own (Antiquities 17:2:4). We notice two things here.

First, we find that it was not only Magi from the East who expected a new king in Judaea, but people in Herod's own realm. Did these Pharisees make their prediction because of what they saw in the sky? We do not normally associate astrology with the Pharisees. But some Jews did look to the sky for revelation, and at Qumran a kind of horoscope has been found among the Dead Sea Scrolls. Josephus relates the belief that astrology came first of all from Abraham. Whether the Pharisees' prediction of a new king was at all sky-related or not, it is in the record. People in Herod's own realm expected a new dynasty at the time of Herod's death, and Herod knew it. All the more reason for Herod to be in fear of a new King of the Jews.

Second, Bogoas' response means this coming king was expected to be a supernatural kind of individual, not limited to what kings on earth had done before. He would be a miracle-working king. Bogoas the eunuch would be granted the ability by this new king to have children of his own. Again, it is in the record that such a person was expected in Herod's own realm, and during Herod's last days.

We will now look closely at the two eclipses that have been proposed as the lunar event preceding Herod's death, and the issues associated with whether either one could be the eclipse of which Josephus writes. Before we do, however, we will recognize that Dag Kihlman has written a book about the Star of Bethlehem which takes the study in new directions. It offers valuable insights, which will be shared later. However, Kihlman does not even mention the eclipse preceding Herod's death. He places the death in 2 B.C., which seems impossible. We will return to Kihlman's assertions later in this chapter.

The Case for 4 B.C.

On the 12th of March in 4 B.C., a lunar eclipse occurred that actually turned none of the moon's surface black, but caused some of the moon to take on a dark red cast. The duration of the eclipse was two hours and 10 minutes. It concluded just before the moon set in the West and the sun rose in the East. That means it was happening when most people were asleep, and it has been argued that most would not have been aware of it at all. While that is not a strong argument, as eclipses go this one was not impressive. The eclipse preceding Herod's death is the only eclipse Josephus mentions in all his historical writings, so one might expect a more spectacular event. That is one of the arguments against the 4 B.C. eclipse. Still, it was an eclipse, and if Josephus includes it because it was considered an omen associated with Herod's punishment of the religious leaders, even a rather insignificant eclipse cannot be ruled out.

Now we must decide whether known events on earth and in the sky at the general time of the 4 B.C. eclipse fit with what Matthew and Luke say about the birth of Christ.

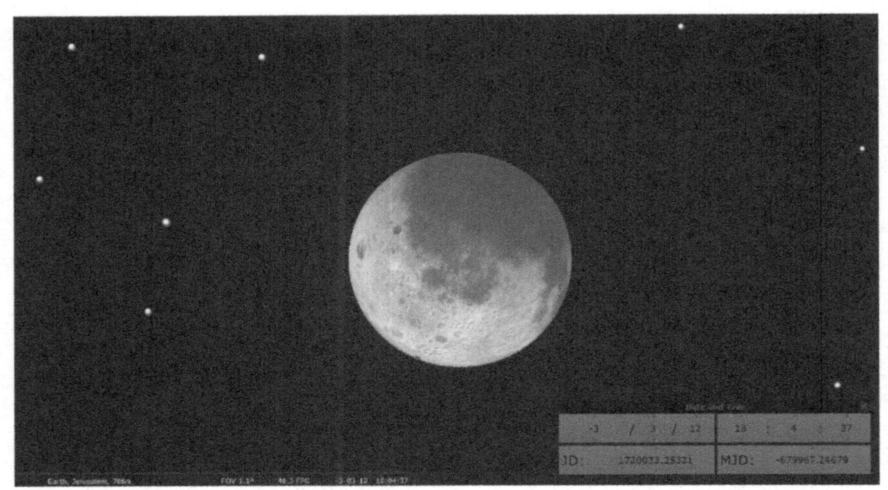

Figure 28. The lunar eclipse of March 12, 4 B.C., as seen from Jerusalem. This image shows the eclipse at its greatest extent. Stellarium software.

What astronomers call the "Great Conjuction" of Saturn, Jupiter, and Mars took place in 7 and 6 B.C. It has long been associated with the Star of Bethlehem by those following the 4 B.C. scenario. It has an interesting history.

In 1604 Johannes Kepler, brilliant astronomer and mathematician, witnessed a conjunction of Saturn and Jupiter. It must have been notable to the people of the time, including astronomers besides Kepler. His associates helped him observe the nightly evolution of the conjunction. Clouds obscured some of this in Prague where Kepler was. A new star, probably a nova, was seen by Kepler's associates near the conjunction. Kepler had recently read a treatise about the Star of Bethlehem, and wondered whether such a planetary occurrence—especially the "new star"—may have been what the Magi saw (Matthew 2).

Kepler was able to compute that this conjunction had occurred in 7 and 6 B.C. Saturn and Jupiter came into conjunction in May/June, September/October, and December of 7 B.C. Early in 6 B.C., Mars joined the massed planets forming a cluster. This has become known as "the great conjunction." Whether it was even visible next to the setting sun is an important question. Still, many have thought this conjunction was the Star of Bethlehem. It occurred in the zodiacal house of Pisces. Pisces has been thought of as the "house of the Hebrews". It may have been, but the evidence we have for this is from medieval times, not before. Saturn is associated with Israel in Amos 5:26 where the prophet chastises the people for their syncretistic practices of worshiping this star god, Kiyyun. Kiyyun is Saturn.

> *"You shall take up Sikkuth your king, and Kiyyun your star-god—your images that you made for yourselves..."* Kiyyun is also known as Rephan in the Greek Septuagint (see Acts 7:42).

Jupiter was regarded as the star (planet) of kings. Among the Romans it was called Jupiter, because Jupiter was regarded as king of the gods. In Babylon it was called Marduk for the same reason. Jupiter had other names as well in Mesopotamia, a dozen of them. Jupiter is the third-brightest object in the night sky after the Moon and Venus. The Fourth Century astrologer Fermicus Maternus related that "...men would be immortal if the favorable influence of Jupiter were never overcome in their charts (Maternus, Firmicus. *Ancient Astrology Theory and Practice. Matheseos Libri VIII, Astrology Classics,* Tr. Jean Rhys Bram. Bel Air, MD: The Astrology Center of America, 1975, p. 43).

One hundred years before Kepler a Jewish scholar, Isaac Abravanel, studied the works of a still earlier scholar, Abraham bar Hiyya. Bar Hiyya concluded that a conjunction of Saturn and Jupiter preceded the giving of the Law to Moses by 83 years in 1395 B.C. Bar Hiyya thought the same conjunction would precede the coming of the Messiah. A Saturn and Jupiter conjunction occurred within Abarvanel's lifetime in 1464 AD, causing him to predict that Messiah would come within 83 years. Abravanel did not know that this conjunction had in fact occurred shortly before the birth of Jesus.

As to the suitability of the massing of the three planets to be the Star of Bethlehem there are serious problems. The Star of Bethlehem stopped in some way above Bethlehem according to Matthew. There is no satisfactory explanation of how these planets together fulfilled this requirement. A few might think of the Star as basically historical, while still allowing its stopping to fall into the category of unhistorical legend. And as already noted, the massing of planets in 7 and 6 B.C. was close to the sun—faint in the sky. Even if the appearance of these planets might have been in the East first, and quite visible, the 7 and 6 B.C. massing of planets does not fulfill the requirements for it to have been in all ways the Star of Bethlehem.

When one reads that Jesus was probably born in 7 or 6 B.C., this conjunction is part of the reason for that conclusion. It has only been pursued because of the eclipse in 4 B.C., requiring some explanation for the Star that can be found in the sky during these earlier years. Though some have argued for it, this massing of planets takes a distant second place to what we will discuss next.

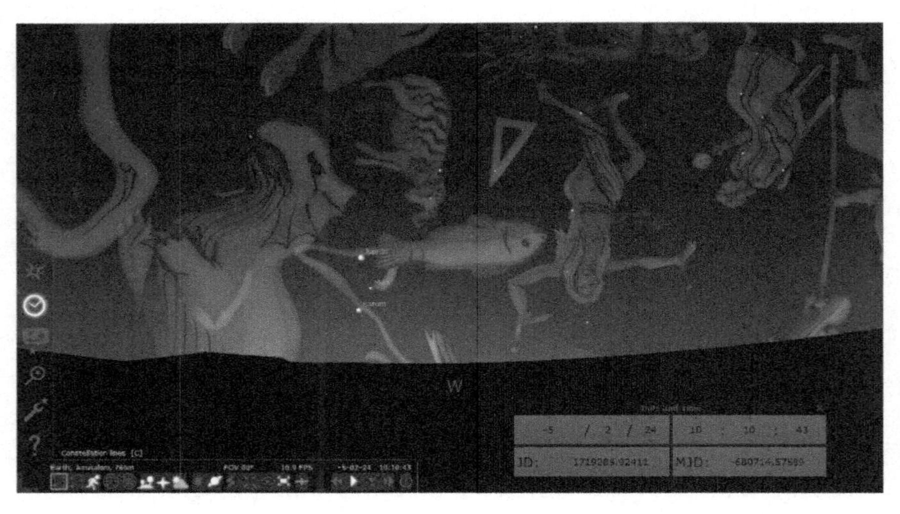

Figure 29. The massing of Jupiter, Saturn, and Mars as it appeared on February 24, 6 BC. The cluster is in Pisces, visible at sunset. Some question whether it could still be seen this close to the setting sun.

The Case for 1 B.C.

The eclipse of January 9/10, 1 B.C., if it is the eclipse of which Josephus writes, opens a new time window for exploration, the time window between the two eclipses, a time window dismissed as too late by those who have placed Herod's death in 4 B.C. This January eclipse was a total lunar eclipse which lasted for three hours and forty minutes. Unlike the March eclipse, the January eclipse was earlier in the night. It took place high overhead, starting before the Moon had reached its zenith in the sky. Though the March eclipse must not be ruled out simply because it was not spectacular, as we said above, the January eclipse was much more likely to have been seen by many people. It is also more likely to have been considered an omen from Heaven against Herod, because the entire surface of the Moon was darkened for most of the duration of the eclipse.

Figure 30. The lunar eclipse of January 10, 1 B.C., as seen from Jerusalem. This image shows the eclipse at its greatest extent. Stellarium software.

Objection #1: The Coins

The dates on coins of Herod's sons have been interpreted to mean that they all began to rule in 4 B.C. Subtracting the highest year number available on a coin from the age of the ruler when he died gives the year 4 B.C. This has been the strongest argument for the assertion that Herod died that year. In fact, the matter is more complicated. We assume that the dates given on coins are factual. In truth, they sometimes convey legal fictions for purposes of propaganda on behalf of the ruler.

The best example of this may come from Herod himself. When he captured Jerusalem from his enemy, Antigonus, and began to rule there as "King of the Jews", Herod issued coins marked Year 3. It had been three years since the Roman Senate made him King. But he had only just begun to rule in Jerusalem when he issued these coins. The coin dates were meant to increase his recognition as a legitimate ruler. The number on the coins corresponded only to a legal fact, not to the experienced reality of anyone who would be using them.

The sons of Herod may have wished to claim more years than they actually ruled as well. We know that Herod changed his will twice before he died. His surviving sons contested the final will before Caesar. Alexander and Aristobulus, who were to rule, were now dead. It is surely conceivable that the surviving sons of Herod would wish to trace their rule from the time Alexander and Aristobulus were first determined to succeed Herod. Now that they were gone, other sons might claim those years. This could explain coins indicating rule from the year 4 B.C., but not actually struck until 1 B.C. Artificial dignity in the form of exaggerated coin dates should have been appealing to Herod's third-choice descendants.

It is also possible that the dates on Herod's sons' coins reflect a tacit claim of co-regency. A co-regency appears to have been in place with Antipater. Josephus reports the following from Antipater at his trial. In claiming that he had nothing to gain by overthrowing his father, Antipater said: "I was a king already," and "...whom thou madest a king in thine own lifetime." Herod had previously stated that he had done this for Antipater (Jewish Wars 1:32). In Antiquities Josephus says "When the affairs of Herod were in the condition I have described, all the public affairs depended upon Antipater (17:2:4).

It is more difficult to make this case for the other sons. But even if all three surviving sons were not technically co-regents with Herod, what matters is what Archelaus, Antipas, and Philip wanted people to think after Herod was gone. Antipater was put to death;

his name was blotted from the record. Could the names of the remaining sons be inserted to fill the legal vacuum of those years when Antipater was co-regent and heir apparent—or from the time of the deaths of the Hasmonean sons? This, too, could explain coin dates that indicate 4 B.C., but only to promote a legal fiction. There are numerous cases of such ante-dating of coins. The Herodian sons would not have been alone in promoting the idea of longer reigns than they in fact enjoyed.

Now, as E. L. Martin brought to our attention (*The Star That Astonished the World,* Second Edition. Academy for Scriptural Knowledge: Portland, Oregon: 1996), a careful study of the oldest manuscripts of Josephus conducted by David W. Beyer ("Josephus Re-examined: Unraveling the Twenty-Second Year of Tiberius" *Chronos, Kairos, Christos Two*, pages 85-96, Ray Summers, Jerry Vardaman. Mercer University Press, 1998) has yielded an important discovery. In some of the oldest manuscripts of Josephus, Herod's son Philip is reported to have died in the twenty-second year of Tiberius, not the twentieth, as newer manuscripts read. Greek numbers are similar to Roman numbers; they are written with letters. A scribal error of omitting one letter would make the difference between twenty-two and twenty. Succeeding scribes could then perpetuate that mistake into the newer manuscripts of Josephus's works.

The matter is not beyond debate. The quality of the Latin manuscripts is at issue. But if Beyer is right, this creates serious problems for those who wish to maintain that 4 B.C. was the year of Herod's death. First, one of the three brothers is now shown to have begun his rule at the end of 2 or in 1 B.C. This is already an argument in favor of a later year for Herod's death. The second problem is: it now appears all the more likely that the other two brothers utilized the legal fiction idea, granting themselves more years on their coins than they actually ruled. In other words, here is an indication that someone was not telling the truth on coins. After all, the three brothers began to rule at the same time after Caesar decided Herod's will. Different starting points for Herod's three sons would be nearly fatal to the coin argument for 4 B.C.

Figure 31. Coin detail of a coin struck by Antipas, one of Herod's three sons who succeeded him as a tetrarch. The letters within the oval on the picture to the left give the date, year 37. Public domain.

Objection #2: The Time Frame

Time frame questions involve a "census" of the world as reported in Luke. They also involve the "governorship" of Quirinius, named in the Gospel of Luke. Further they involve Quintilius Varus, the Governor of Syria who was present with Herod just before he died. The time between the eclipse and the following Passover is yet another matter of interest, because Josephus says Herod died before the Passover, and that a number of associated things took place prior to his burial, also before Passover. Was there enough time in 4 B.C., or 1 B.C., for all these things to take place between the eclipse and the following Passover? That is a subject we will not revisit here, but bear in mind there are issues arising from it that point toward 1 B.C. as the year of Herod's death.

So we must now look *inside* this new window of time, between 4 B.C. and 1 B.C. What was happening on earth, and what can we find in the sky if we use computer technology to recreate the motions of the planets? What will emerge from our investigation of the time frame between 4 B.C. and 1 B.C.?

The Census

We have already seen that Josephus reported a gathering of loyalty oaths in Herod's kingdom sometime just prior to Herod's death. In Antiquities of the Jews XVII:2:4. Josephus tells of six thousand Pharisees who refused to swear their allegiance to Herod and Caesar. Herod's sister-in-law, the wife of his brother Pheroras, paid a fine for them all.

We can say more about loyalty oaths at this time. We have information from Augustus Caesar himself. Near his mausoleum were inscribed his Res Gestae, the list of the accomplishments of Augustus Caesar. He states there that the entire people of Rome granted him the title, Father of the Country. It already begins to look as if a loyalty oath was taken across the Roman world to honor the Emperor. He received this honor in February of 2 B.C., about a year before the time we are exploring for the death of Herod. So, the loyalty oaths must have been gathered just prior to 2 B.C. On the occasion of the Emperor's 25th anniversary, and in the 750th year of the City of Rome, this title was formally bestowed. We might expect that from region to region across the Empire an oath to the local rulers would have been added.

None of this would or could have been a secret from the Emperor. He had declined the title once before this. He was involved; his permission was surely required. The order ultimately came from him. This brings to mind the opening statement of Luke 2: "In those days a decree went out from Caesar Augustus that all the world should be registered." In years past most took this as a reference to an actual Roman census. The 8 B.C. census was the candidate, and it roughly fit the scenario of Herod's death falling in 4 B.C. This became an additional argument for placing the birth of Jesus in a range of years before 4 B.C. But the word used by Luke is *apographé*. It means registration, and is not limited to the census.

E. L. Martin (*The Star That Astonished the World*) offers additional information to support this empire-wide loyalty oath gathering as the registration of which Luke writes.

- Armenia Moses of Khorene who compiled Armenia's first history said sources available to him showed that a registration brought Roman agents "to Armenia, bringing the image of Augustus Caesar, which they set up in every temple." This was in the second year of Abgar, king of

Armenia. That translates to 3 B.C. Clearly, people taking the oath were expected to travel to where the images of Caesar were set up. There is no mention that only Roman citizens took this oath, as in the case of a formal Roman census. This is consistent with Luke's account, that "each went to his own city." That would probably not be true for an actual Roman census.

- An inscription found in Paphlagonia This inscription tells of an oath of obedience "taken by the inhabitants of Paphlagonia and the Roman businessmen dwelling among them." The date is 3 B.C. Again, this involves all people in the region, and not just Roman citizens.
- Orosius Paul Orosius was one of the first to write a history of the church, though Eusebius is better-known. He tells that Caesar "ordered that a census be taken of each province everywhere and that all men be enrolled. ... This is the earliest and most famous public acknowledgment which marked Caesar as the first of all men and the Romans as lords of the world, a published list of all men entered individually ... This first and greatest census was taken, since in this one name of Caesar all the peoples of the great nations took oath, and at the same time, through the participation in the census, were made apart of one society..." Orosius, VI.22 and VII.2

Quirinius

Luke says the registration happened when Quirinius was Governor of Syria. At least, most Bibles are translated that way. Some have made the case that Luke's text should be worded as follows: "This was the registration *before* Quirinius was governing in Syria." Why "before"? It looks like this translation really comes from bias on the part of believing translators, done to save Luke from what many have considered an historical mistake. There is no evidence that P. Sulpicius Quirinius was Governor of Syria at this time. Shown below is R. E. Brown's list as compiled from reading the text of Josephus:

R. E. Brown Birth of the Messiah p. 550

23-13 B.C.:	M. Agrippa
ca. 10 B.C.:	M. Titius
9-6 B.C.:	S. Sentius Saturninus
6-4 B.C. or later:	Quintilius (or Quinctilius) Varus
1 B.C. to ca. A.D. 4:	Gaius Caesar
A.D. 4-5:	L. Volusius Saturninus
A.D. 6 to after 7:	P. Sulpicius Quirinius

Quirinius does not appear until A.D. 6. This is when Josephus tells us Quirinius was sent into Judea to take a census and liquidate the holdings of the now-deposed Archelaus, Herod's son. Some scholars have said Luke thought the 6 AD census was what brought Joseph and Mary to Bethlehem, and therefore Luke was off by a decade for the birth of Jesus. Other scholars have countered that Luke is known to have been a careful historian. They also say that gaps exist in the list of Governors of Syria. Perhaps Quirinius was there during one of those gaps as Governor, and this is what Luke is telling us.

The 6 AD census almost led to a war. It was the cool-headed influence of the High Priest that kept the peace. For the first time Judea came under direct Roman rule; that was a hard fact for the Jews to accept. From this moment on a Roman ruler would preside. No client king, ethnarch, or tetrarch would be the final authority any longer.

This brings us back to the translation "before". Some object that Luke had no reason to say or mean "before", so we should not impose that meaning when translating Luke's Greek. This is only an attempt to "save the credibility of Luke", they say. The word *prōtā* does not normally mean "before", but "first". While those who have argued for translating the text with "before" seem not to have thought of it, the census event in 6 AD, was traumatic for everyone in Judea. It was in their minds a pivotal event, like a December 7 or a September 11. Realizing this, it makes sense that Luke may have been differentiating the prior registration from that later, infamous one when Quirinius *was* Governor of Syria. In other words: "This was the (earlier, first, lesser known) registration before that (infamous, well-known) census which happened when Quirinius was Governor of Syria." That is one way to deal with the Quirinius problem. It may not be particularly strong. Still, it cannot be dismissed.

There is still another way to approach the Quirinius issue. It also concerns the meaning of a word. Luke does not say Quirinius was the Governor of Syria, though the King James Version and many versions since have translated his text that way. Luke uses a participle of the verb for ruling/governing (*hāgemoneúontos*). We cannot press the meaning of Luke's words beyond: This was the first registration when Quirinius *was governing in Syria*. Some have asserted that Quirinius was prosecuting a war elsewhere in Galatia (the Homonadensan War), or busy with something else, but was technically the Governor. In fact, he need not have been the Roman Governor at all for Luke to be correct. What might Quirinius have been doing in an official governing role if he was not serving as Governor? One plausible answer: securing the loyalty oaths to Caesar from the people of Syria, and perhaps beyond.

Justin Martyr, writing in the Second Century, said Quirinius was Rome's first *Procurator* in Judaea (Apology 1.34). That is significant, because a procurator could be working simultaneously with a Governor in a province. The evolution of changes in Roman government offices is complex: the *cursus honorum*, procurator, prefect, governor, etc. Whose responsibilities were military? Whose responsibilities were monetary? And did roles change with time? Could a governor ever serve twice in the same post? Besides, there were places where there was one official who answered to the Senate, and another who answered to the Emperor. Suffice it to say here that the original meaning of "procurator" was: manager, overseer, agent, deputy. In advance of the Father of the Country honor, with its February 2 B.C. deadline, someone had to secure the loyalty oaths of the people of Syria. It makes sense in view of what Justin Martyr wrote that Quirinius was that person. Thus, his absence on the list of Governors is not a problem. Quirinius was governing in Syria.

A critical reader might respond: But Varus *is* a problem. Josephus has Herod in conversation with Varus within a week before Herod's death. We know that Varus was Governor of Syria from 6-4 A.D. Is that not the death blow to the argument that Herod died in 1 B.C.?

So it would seem. But one particular stone held in the Vatican Museum may be the answer to this problem. It was discovered in 1764. It has inscribed upon it words about a person who was twice Governor of Syria. The name of the person is broken off. The grammar of what's left has been debated, but A. N. Sherwin-White says it speaks of a person who was twice Governor of Syria, as opposed to a Governor twice, once in Syria, and once somewhere else. Of course, some scholars have been most eager to say on the basis of the stone that Quirinius was Governor twice, but what little is written on the stone does not conform to the career of Quirinius (Sherwin-White, *Roman Law and Roman Society in the New Testament.* pp. 162-169). It is still called the sepulchral inscription of Quir*inius* at the Vatican Museum where it is kept, but it most probably had nothing to do with Quirinius.

The stone was found near the entrance to the remains of an old Roman villa. That villa had long been considered the home of Quintilius Varus. The events related on the stone do conform to his career.

What would it mean if Varus had been Governor of Syria twice? First, it would make perfect sense, because these were threatening times in Roman Judea. Keeping a person in place who already knew the political and military context made more sense than replacing him with someone at a difficult time. War had in fact broken out, known as the Varus War. Some historians object that governors never governed the same place twice, but the stone indicates that somebody did.

Here is the revised list of Governors of Syria as presented by Jack Finegan:

TABLE 147. *Revised List of Governors of Syria*

B.C./AD	Governor
Prior to 7 B.C.	M. Titius
7 or 6—4 B.C.	P. Quintilius Varus
4 B.C.—2 B.C.	C. Sentius Saturninus
2 B.C.—1 A.D.	P. Quintillius Varus
A.D. 1-4	C. Caesar

From Jack Finegan, Handbook of Biblical Chronology, Revised Edition, Hendrickson 1998, p. 304.

In this reconstruction, Varus (1) still occupies those years as Governor which were never contested in 7 or 6 to 4 B.C., but (2) also the time in which the new proposal for Herod's death in 1 B.C., requires. His earlier rule ceases to be a problem for re-dating the death of Herod.

Notice that the second term of Varus in Syria in the revised list follows Saturninus' two-year term. Tertullian in the Second Century was one of those claiming that Jesus was born in 3/2 B.C. Tertullian was a lawyer in Carthage. He knew and practiced the Roman system of law. Tertullian said the Roman records related to Jesus' birth existed for his doubting debate opponent, Marcion, to see, and that they were obtained in the governorship of Saturninus (Against Marcion, 4:19). Tertullian without doubt knew Luke's Gospel. He knew what Luke had said about Quirinius, but saw no contradiction in saying Saturninus had been Governor in 3/2 B.C., when he believed Jesus had been born. He obviously believed Quirinius had been governing in a different capacity around 2 B.C. This serves to confirm further that Varus served as Governor twice, and Quirinius governed as procurator during the time of Jesus' birth which was in 3/2 B.C.

The Apple

We offer one more item as evidence that Herod died in 1 B.C. Recall that five days before his death, Herod impulsively attempted to end his life. He asked for an apple and a knife, but he really meant to use the knife to take his own life.

Refrigeration is a modern reality. Ancient citizens of the Mideast did at times use ice in beverages. One can imagine that transporting ice or snow and keeping it from melting for any length of time was nearly impossible for them. Produce had to be stored in cool places like caves or store rooms.

If the eclipse before Herod's death was in 4 B.C., the time was mid-March. An experiment with an ordinary apple kept in my unheated shop demonstrated that the apple did not survive even past the first week of March (see photos). But if this event happened in 1 B.C., the eclipse it followed was in January. Apples would still have been available and edible.

Figure 32. Herod requested an apple five days before his death, at the approximate time of the lunar eclipse reported in Josephus. If this occurred in 1 B.C., when the eclipse took place in January, the apple might have appeared as in the picture on the left. This apple was stored in an unheated room, similar to a cool cave in biblical times. But if the year of Herod's death was 4 B.C., the eclipse was in mid-March. The picture on the right is of the same apple, but it shows the results of the passing of time. Thus, the detail about Herod's request for an apple argues that he died in 1 B.C., not 4.

Before we move on to more matters of what was happening on the earth and in the sky, let's review what we have covered so far. First, there is a serious case to be made for Herod's death in 4 B.C., and truly fine scholars have reached that conclusion. But an old tradition from the hands of early Christians says otherwise, placing Jesus' birth later than 4 B.C. Are they all simply wrong? Normally historians would not reach such a conclusion. Upon closer examination we find answers to every objection against a 1 B.C.

death year for Herod. In the matter of Herod's sons' coins, it now appears that two of the sons were adding years to their reigns that may have been legally theirs, but not historically theirs. Nothing has been brought forward weighty enough to overturn the united voices of the early church fathers. Jesus was born in 3 or 2 B.C. We have not listed all the arguments in support of 1 B.C. as the year of Herod's death. There are others given in the books cited already.

One of the names most associated with matters of biblical chronology is Jack Finegan. He wrote a compendium of helpful information and published it in 1964. The title suggests a short, cursory volume: *Handbook of Biblical Chronology*. But the book is amazingly thorough on matters of both New and Old Testament events and dates. In 1999 Finegan published a revised edition. One of the main reasons for this was that he had changed his mind about when Jesus was born. In 1964 he had accepted the 4 B.C., death year for Herod, with a nativity year before that. When he learned of some of the matters we have discussed here in these pages, Professor Finegan was persuaded that Jesus was born in 3 or 2 B.C.

The Politico-Celestial State of Affairs in 2 B.C.

Figure 33. Roman Empire, left; Parthian Empire, center; Han Empire, right. Gabagool, CC BY 3.0 <https://creativecommons.org/licenses/by/3.0>, via Wikimedia Commons.

The vast and mighty Empire of Rome extended eastward from Britain, Spain, and Germany some two thousand miles to the Empire of Parthia. These two great political entities did not actually border each other, but they maintained a peace in tension across the upper part of the Arabian Peninsula. Western readers usually have little knowledge of Parthia, because they are inheritors of Greek and Roman civilization, not Parthian. In fact, Parthia was expansive and formidable, just as Rome. Through the years the uneasy peace prevailed between them for the most part, but significant battles happened where the empires were in proximity, like the way earthquakes happen where tectonic plates push against one another.

The capital of Parthia was Ctesophon. It stood on the bank of the Tigris River, about twenty miles from modern Bagdad. Academic discussions of the Magi we meet in Matthew 2 usually report correctly that Magi might have been found anywhere, East or West, from Rome to India. Therefore, the Magi might have come from anywhere east of biblical Judea. (They are identified as being "from the East".) But Magi were present to a degree in Parthia not found in other places. While an individual Magus, or a group of Magi, might be found living in anywhere, in the Parthian Empire, the Magi were part of one house of the government. We will have more to say about that below. So when we investigate the visit of the Magi in Matthew 2, we cannot rule out any point of origin for them, as long as it is East, but Ctesiphon, Parthia, should stand out as a highly likely point of origin. A long journey undertaken by Magi is also better explained as the work of government ambassadors on a mission, rather than self-motivated, wealthy individuals.

A Poisoning in Parthia

In late 3 or early 2 B.C. a new king claimed the throne of the Parthian Empire. Behind this event was a woman who was not of Parthian (Arsacid) descent at all, but presumably Italian. She had been a slave whom Augustus Caesar sent years earlier to the Parthian King, Phraates IV. Then she had been known as Thermusa; now she was Musa, who ascended through the ranks of the concubines until she became the Queen of the Parthians. Musa had a son by Phraates IV named Phraataces (a diminutive form of Phraates). She convinced the king to send all his sons except Phraataces to Rome for their well-being. When they were gone, Musa and Phraataces did to Phraates IV what he had done to his father Orodes before him. They killed him. They used poison. Phraates seized the throne to become Phraates V, and married Musa, his mother.

Parthia was ruled by its King, and also by the Megistanes, an institution of two houses. The first house of the Megistanes was comprised of male members of the royal family. The second was the house of the Sophi and the Magi. It was the duty of the Sophi and Magi house in Parthia to approve or disapprove rulers, including the Kings. But all other sons of Phraates IV were absent, and could not be considered for potential rule by the king-making body, the House of the Sophi and Magi.

It is difficult to imagine that the Magi House desired this non-Parthian Queen and her weak son, who had become murderers in order to usurp power. About six years later Phraates V was deposed. He and Musa fled to Rome. History shows how undesirable they had become in Parthia.

Figure 34. Phraates V left and Musa right. Classical Numismatic Group, Inc. http://www.cngcoins.com, CC BY-SA 3.0<http://creativecommons.org/licenses/by-sa/3.0/>, via Wikimedia Commons

A Threatening Time

Parthia was now destabilized as Phraates V and Musa seized power. Next Phraates V moved into Armenia. This was a direct challenge to Rome. Augustus considered Armenia his. Loyalty oaths to Caesar had only recently been secured there from the whole population, as we saw. In 1 B.C. Augustus would send his adopted son Gaius on a military tour of the East. Gaius was young, and not ready to assume the role of Emperor. He had been fast-tracked through the *cursus honorum* (progression of government offices) so he could assume greater responsibilities, though he was not yet twenty years old. Augustus believed he had no one else to rely upon. He had to confront Parthia and its King. All people could see that a war between the great empires was likely.

Gaius was accompanied by Marcus Lollius, who was to be his advisor. Others of rank and dignity also accompanied Gaius, including Sulpicius Quirinius. Lollius was accused of crimes during the tour, ordered to commit suicide, and replaced by Quirinius. Gaius' official title at this time was Governor of Syria. (This was another time when it could be said that Quirinius was governing in Syria). Augustus had written to Phraates V, refusing to address him as King. "King of Kings" was the recognized title Phraates V demanded. Gaius was marching toward the capital of Parthia with the legions he had brought with him from the Danube. *Clearly he was preparing to invade the Parthian Empire.* In 1 AD a peace settlement was reached as the legions stood on one side of the Euphrates River, the Parthian armies on the other side, and Gaius with Phraates V on an island between them. Phraates V renounced any claim on Armenia. In return he was recognized as the King of Parthia by Rome.

Disaster had been averted this time. Magi in Parthia must have remained concerned about the irreparable damage Phraates V could do to their Empire in days to come.

Mesopotamian Sky Lore

Until recently, discussions of the Magi and the Star of Bethlehem have said little about Mesopotamian astrology. Now Dag Kihlman has shed light on this very important source of knowledge. (*The Star of Bethlehem and Babylonian Astrology* (Trollhätten, Sweden: Dag Kihlman, 2018). Kihlman introduces the documents specialists in Mesopotamian astrology today call "scriptures" or "canon". These were primarily lists of omens which were cataloged and preserved for centuries, going back to the ancient Assyrians and Sumerians.

The *Enuma Anu Enlil* is the primary source for us. This is a set of tablets written in cuneiform in protasis/apodasis form, if/then. For instance: (prodasis) if a certain kind of planetary conjunction occurs, (apodasis) prices for grain will be low. Additional letters from Mesopotamian scholars also inform our investigation. These have been collected, edited, and made available for a non-specialist audience.

The purpose of the sky omens was not to announce to people the ways they would be imprisoned by fate, but rather to offer an escape. Omens were warnings. They were studied to avoid bad outcomes. This avoidance was accomplished with rituals and offerings to the gods, or by waiting out a threatening period of time. It was also done by substituting a false king called "the farmer" when an omen warmed of disaster for the King. The substitute king would be the one to suffer the disaster. Then the true King would re-occupy the throne, and the farmer would be put to death. These ancients were truly serious about their omens.

The omens were simple, though they needed to be interpreted for each individual situation. Sometimes omens were in conflict. Sometimes there simply were no omens to behold. Omens were also often territorial. "Traditional Babylonian astrology differs in two important aspects from the other Babylonian divinatory disciplines: it is geographically oriented—many of its apodoses apply to specific countries, cities or nations —and it is almost wholly concerned with the welfare of the state and the king as persona publica." (Ulla Koch-Westenholz, [*Mesopotamian Astrology: An Introduction to Babylonian and Assyrian Celestial Divination* p. 19.])

Kihlman is right when he says we must look to Mesopotamian astrology if we want to understand what the Magi saw in the stars. But he does not appear to be open enough to the likelihood of changes in eastern astrology due to the passing of time and to the influence of western astrology. The old omens as found in *Enuma Anu Enlil* and Assyrian letters must have retained their classical status, but they were not consulted as though no new insights mattered. Historians chart the transformation of Mesopotamian astrology over the centuries, and they agree that changes did take place.

Figure 35. Armenian, similar in appearance to a magus. Gaidzakian, Ohan, 1837-1914. [from old catalog], No restrictions, via Wikimedia Commons.

When eastern astrology reached the West, starting with Berossus in the Third Century B.C., western practitioners developed the horoscope. The future for the individual calculated on the basis of the positions of the stars and planets at the moment of conception or birth took astrology to a wider audience. The realization that the motions of the stars could be calculated in advance made astrology among westerners more an art of applying over-arching, repetitive cosmic principles than apprehending specific warnings from the gods. This is not to say that eastern astrologers did not apply mathematics to their study of the sky. Our system of 360 degrees within a circle goes back to them, and to their division of the day into twenty-four hours. Eastern astrologers did compute positions of planets in advance, but westerners developed this in a different direction.

East and West developed their own lore, and went in somewhat different directions. Still, what they had in common remained considerable. So we must proceed recognizing that eastern and western astrologers might reach somewhat different conclusions about what they saw in the sky in 3 and 2 B.C. Certainly, any group of three astrologers anywhere could reach up to three conclusions about what sights in the sky meant. But there were important things held in common, like the importance of Jupiter and Venus, the divisions of the world, and the way omens addressed the nations. And if the events in the sky were rare enough, spectacular enough, we might expect astrologers from East and West to be equally amazed, and reach similar conclusions about what those events signified.

Birth Announcement

Two questions need answers as we go forward. (1) What reason do we have to think that any sign in the sky within the years 4 to 1 B.C., would be interpreted as announcing a royal birth? (2) If such a sign were to be found, why would it be understood as pertaining to Syria?

Here we find no direct, applicable interpretation of omens from the Mesopotamian lists. It must be understood that a good deal of the cuneiform on the stone tablets is effaced. It is possible that such an omen once occupied its place in those scriptures, but we know of no such omens specifically.

The classical astrology as preserved in *Enuma Anu Enlil* from centuries earlier maintained its place of respect in Mesopotamia, though newer methods and interests were now being applied. When an unusual happening in the sky took place, and newer methods offered no immediate wisdom, the classical doctrines were still there to be considered. All eastern Magi aware of their own classical omen documents would have known of the following passage:

> *"If Venus enters Jupiter (UD.AL.Tar): the king of Akkad will die, the dynasty will change, either a soldier will go out or the enemy will send a message (asking for peace) to the land."* Reiner, Erica and David Pingree. *Babylonian Planetary Omens Part Three, Cuneiform Monographs 11* (Groningen, Styx Publications, 1998, p. 93.

Koch-Westenholz says this of the eastern system: "In astrology, an omen was often seen to pertain to one of the four geographical entities Akkad (South), Subartu (North), Elam (East) and Amurru (West). To the Assyrians, omens pertaining to both Akkad and Subartu referred to 'us', at least in times when the Assyrian king was the overlord of Akkad, i.e. Babylonia as well. Elam and *Amurru referred to 'the enemy'",* p. 98. [italics mine].

If we return to Matthew 2 we find the Magi saying: "…we have seen his star in the East, and have come to worship him (2:2)." This sentence has the Greek expression *en tā enatolā* for "in the east". This is not the usual way to indicate the east, as in eastern regions (which is *anatolōn*). It uses a participial form of the verb *anatellein*, which means "to rise". The Magi actually say: "We have seen his star at its rising." Without doubt this refers to what astronomers call heliacal rising, a concept well-known from the earliest days of astrology.

As the sun travels through the sky over the course of the year the atmosphere makes seeing stars during the day impossible. But each day, before the sun rises, a new sliver of the night sky (1/365¼ of it) becomes visible over the eastern horizon ahead of the bright sun. When a star or planet is first seen ahead of the rising sun, this is its heliacal rise.

On August 13, 3 B.C., Jupiter and Venus appeared in heliacal rise. They appeared extremely close to each other in the sky—almost touching. Kihlman is probably right that eastern Magi would have been alarmed by this. Venus entering Jupiter was a warning that their King was in danger, and that it would be advisable to send messengers to ask for peace in the land of the enemy.

Shortly after the appearance of this omen, the poisoning in Parthia brought Phraates V and Musa to the throne. The Magi would have considered their classical texts to have rightly foretold what happened. The enemy had actually been from within the Empire, and the dynasty did in some manner change, because Musa was not of Roman descent. The old King was dead; a new King now reigned.

Jupiter continued moving through the night sky toward the bright star Regulus in Leo. The classical texts from the ancient past said:

> *"And the matter of the planet Jupiter is as follows: If it turns back out of the Breast of Leo, this is ominous. It is written in the Series as follows: 'If Jupiter passes Regulus and gets ahead of it, and afterwards Regulus, which it passed and got ahead of, stays within in its setting, someone will rise, kill the king, and seize the throne.' This aforesaid is the only area which is taken as bad if Jupiter retrogrades there. Wherever else it might turn, it may freely do so, there is not a word about it."* [Simo Parpola, *Letters from Assyrian and Babylonian Scholars,* SAA 10 (Helsinki: Helsinki University Press, 1993), pp. 9–10 rev. 12–22.]

The sky event described in this Mesopotamian astrological passage did in fact take place in 3 and 2 B.C. Jupiter moved within the borders of the Lion, Leo. Within Leo shines Regulus, one of the four brightest stars in the entire sky. From night to night the royal planet approached the fixed royal star more closely until it passed above it (9-14-3 B.C.). Then, Jupiter reached its station, its stopping point (11-27-3 B.C.). Gradually, Jupiter reversed direction and moved back to Regulus (2-17-2 B.C.). After reaching its second station, or stopping point (3-27-2 B.C.), Jupiter resumed its course eastward (5-8-2 B.C.). The second stopping point found Jupiter back outside the Lion, just as described in the omens text. The elapsed time for the three conjunctions was almost eight months.

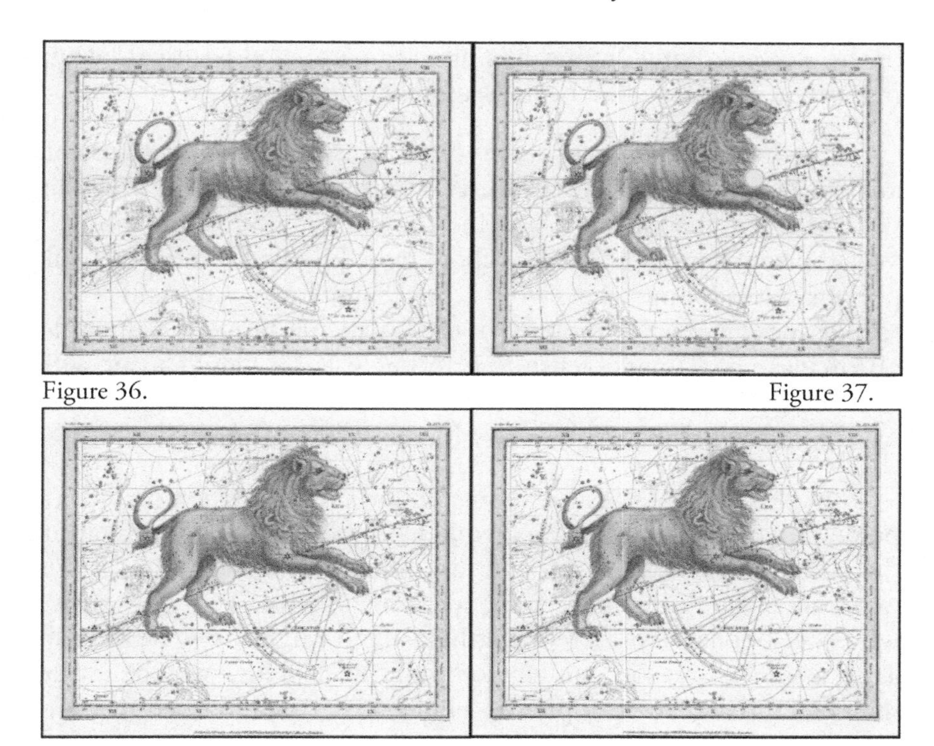

Figure 36. Figure 37.

Figure 38. Figure 39.

Figure 36: Jupiter approaches Regulus in Leo, August 22, 3 B.C. Mercury and Venus have already passed.
Figure 37: Jupiter meets Regulus on September 14, 3 B.C.
Figure 38: Jupter reaches its station and stops against the background of the fixed stars, November 25, 3 B.C.
Figure 39: On March 27, 2 B.C., Jupiter reaches its second station, having retrograded past Regulus and "come out of the heart of the lion."

Amateur astronomers all know that Jupiter retrogrades about every nine months for a period of about four months. But it does not always retrograde in Leo, passing Regulus. These events are much rarer.

Remember, the time was 3 and 2 B.C., and we are considering this to be the probable time of Jesus' birth, as well as the time of the "the Star of Bethlehem". At this very time one omen in the sky involving Jupiter had already paralleled political events in Parthia. The King had been assassinated and replaced.

Now another sky event invoked a passage from the classical, ancient lore of the Magi. Jupiter's retrogression from Regulus warned that someone "will rise, kill the king, and seize the throne." Was the new King, Phraates V, about to be killed? From a practical, political standpoint, that would not have been surprising. His recklessness shown in the invasion of Armenia brought a threat to all of Parthia. It made sense that the new King would meet with disaster, as the retrogression of Jupiter from Leo had warned. Parthia was on the brink of a major war with the Roman Empire!

This ancient passage about Jupiter's retrogression includes a potentially important item: *someone will rise.* This is not present in the other omen about Venus entering Jupiter. The meanings for this expression would include: someone will be born. This one-to-rise who will oppose the current Parthian King might be a child now. This would be reason enough for Magi to consider whether what they had already seen, Jupiter in heliacal rise, had marked the new king's birth.

We should be open to the possibility that Magi would recognize or even expect a child king. Though advisors accompanied child kings and assisted them in making decisions, such kings include Egypt's King Tutankhamun who began ruling at age nine, Joash who began to rule at age six, and Josiah who ruled at age ten. Of special interest is Shapur II. Though he lived later (309-379) in the successor to the Parthian Empire, he was king from birth. Legend even has it that he was coronated *in utero* when the crown was place on his mother's stomach. The Zoroastrian hope of a coming Saoshyant world-savior includes a discussion of his supernatural birth—he would not become the Saoshyant only later as an adult. So, the idea of a king from birth was not at all unthinkable in precisely that part of the world we are considering as the likely home of the Magi in Matthew's Gospel.

A Universal King?

One further idea within Mesopotamian astrology deserves consideration here. This is the theoretical concept of the universal king. From the Third Millennium B.C. there seems to be a recognition of a kind of rule exceeding normal kingship. The title "King of the Entirety" emerged somewhat later. Still later, in the Neo-Babylonian and Persian Empires, the titles for kings implied that the universality of the god Ashur raised one king above other kings. These titles were: "King of Kings" and "King of the Land". This amounts to a claim exceeding normal kingship. (Personal communication from Assyriologist, Dr. John P. Nielsen.)

We have shown that the Magi in Parthia now found themselves with a new and dangerous King, with no others of the royal family present to challenge him for the throne. That choice would otherwise have been the Magis' to make. Might they have entertained the possibility of a universal king who might stand above theirs, and all others as well? This would have been a never-before-considered possibility, but the visible union of Jupiter and Venus which we are about to consider was a never-before-seen event.

Jupiter had now been involved in two spectacular sky-events. Each had warned of disaster for the king in the East. The first omen had already proven true. Now the new king was in danger, and from one who will "rise up". The connection of Jupiter with that king was now becoming apparent. Jupiter was the one common actor to the sky phenomena observed so far.

We have followed the retrogression of Jupiter over the bright star Regulus. Both before and after these conjunctions in Leo, Jupiter and Venus came into very close conjunctions. The first was in heliacal rise. The second was a most-amazing conjunction that brought the two planets together so that they appeared to have fused into one light. It happened June 17, 2 B.C. It appeared at sunset above the western horizon. With that in mind, we look again at the omen that had already come true once:

> *"If Venus enters Jupiter (UD.AL.Tar): the king of Akkad will die, the dynasty will change, either a soldier will go out or the enemy will send a message (asking for peace) to the land."* Reiner and Pingree (1998), p. 93.

Recall that "the enemy" includes Amurru, the region encompassing Herod's Judaea. This is Kihlman's point. But the king of Akkad had already in fact died, and the dynasty did to some degree change in Parthia, with the Roman Musa now the Queen. The directive attached to this omen was to send a soldier to ask for peace. This might prevent devastation at the hand of others in the near future.

Figure 40. The June 17, 2 BC conjunction of Jupiter and Venus. Such close conjunctions as this are centuries apart and most spectacular. The two planets were indistinguishable to the eye. Stellarium.

A sky event spectacular enough to be associated with a unique individual was the conjunction of Jupiter and Venus on June 17, 2 B.C. No magus living had seen such a sight. Conjunctions like this are centuries apart. A most-unusual display in the heavens could be taken as the sign of a birth or conception in progress somewhere. Magi did not normally think this way, especially in the East. But some sky events would have demanded it. The Jupiter Venus conjunction of June 17, 2 B.C., would be the kind of sky event to cause Magi to suspect that a world ruler was being conceived or born somewhere in the world. They were already aware of their omen warning: someone will rise. The signs were amenable to a theory that a universal king was entering the world.

One region's bad omen is another region's good omen. The Magi of the Parthian Megistanes reasoned that a king was rising in Ammuru who would end the current dynasty in Akkad unless steps were taken to secure peace. The threats shown in the sky toward Akkad were simultaneously signs of the best possible fortune for those in the West. The meaning of Jupiter's presence in the series of omens made it clear *in retrospect*: this was the star of the King coming from Amurru. Jupiter was associated now with the king-to-rise in the West. It was time to heed the omens and make peace. The Magi would have reached the conclusion they reported to Herod: we have seen his star at its rising.

Next in the Sky

> *And a great sign appeared in heaven: a woman clothed with the sun, with the moon under her feet, and on her head a crown of twelve stars.* [2] *She was pregnant and was crying out in birth pains and the agony of giving birth.* [3] *And another sign appeared in heaven: behold, a great red dragon, with seven heads and ten horns, and on his heads seven diadems.* [4] *His tail swept down a third of the stars of heaven and cast them to the earth. And the dragon stood before the woman who was about to give birth, so that when she bore her child he might devour it.* [5] *She gave birth to a male child, one who is to rule all the nations with a rod of iron, but her child was caught up to God and to his throne,* [6] *and the woman fled into the wilderness, where she has a place prepared by God, in which she is to be nourished for 1,260 days.* Revelation 12:1-6

New Testament scholars sometimes apply a "criterion of authenticity" known as: multiple attestation. This happens in Gospel studies when a saying of Jesus is found in more than one independent stream of tradition. For instance, if the Synoptic Gospels, and John or Paul present something Jesus said, like his words over the bread and cup for example, those words are multiply attested. If Acts and Josephus both say John the Baptist was arrested and killed by Herod Antipas, that report is multiply attested. When more than one independent source says that something happened, the historian considers it more likely to be true.

We introduce now a case of multiple attestation that is most relevant and important to our investigation of the Star of Bethlehem. Its value as multiple attestation has not been recognized. This discovery requires us to make an abrupt detour in the sky. We must refocus our attention from Jupiter, appearing in heliacal rise with Venus, and then with Regulus in Leo, to the adjacent constellation, Virgo. *We can recreate through astronomical retro-calculation the appearance of Virgo at exactly the time of the first Jupiter Regulus conjunction.* When we do, we suddenly find ourselves in the presence of an image from the twelfth chapter of Revelation. Virgo, with the sun shining in her torso, the new moon near her feet, and Jupiter, Mercury, and Venus near her head making twelve stars when added to the nine in Leo, exactly matches the Woman in Revelation 12.

The last item, the twelve stars near the Woman's head, helps fix the time, because the presence of the three planets, Jupiter, Venus, and Mercury, near her head is far from a usual occurrence. Colin Nicholl (*The Great Christ Comet: Revealing the True Star of Bethlehem*. Wheaton, Illinois: Crossway, 2015.) says on the contrary that twelve actual stars, not planets, are always in the crown of Virgo, but that is due in part to his positioning of the constellation in the sky. He accepts a configuration of the asterism in Virgo which finds her seated, so that her head is lower. If he is right, this would remove the starry crown from the evidence for dating the Virgo configuration to September 3, B.C. But some of those twelve stars claimed by Nicholl to be the crown barely meet the commonly held threshold of visibility, a 6.5 magnitude.

Nicholl claims that using the nine stars in Leo, plus the three planets present in 3 B.C., to make up the crown takes us too far beyond the constellation Virgo. But the placement of the stars in the crown does not have to be particularly reasonable to be what John's vision means. The sun is not actually in the figure of the Woman, only close. The moon is not directly under her feet, only close. For the stars to be only close to her head should not invalidate them as part of the crown. Further, if the locations of the sun and moon are meant to give us at least a general time—like when we say "the big hand is on the 12 and the little hand is on the 9" —we would expect the presence of the twelve stars to indicate a time also. That is only true if the twelve stars are Jupiter, Mercury, and Venus, plus the nine stars of Leo. Why would the crown stars even be mentioned along with the sun and moon, if they did not include the three planets whose presence indicated a specific time?

Even if Nicholl is right about the twelve stars, the times when the sun was in Virgo and the moon was at her feet leave us with only two choices at the end of the reign of Herod the Great. The next earlier case was in 6 B.C. (September 15). That fits the view that Herod died in 4 B.C., but we have presented evidence to show that Herod died in 1 B.C. We conclude that September 11, 3 B.C. was the time of this appearance of the Woman in the sky as described in Revelation 12, even if we base our conclusion only on the locations of the sun and moon, regardless of which stars made up the twelve around her head.

Matthew 2 gives us two events that may also be dated by means of computer technology, not available to people of ancient times. These are the heliacal rising of Jupiter with Venus in 3 B.C. ("We have seen his star at its rising"), and the stopping of the star over Bethlehem in 2 B.C. ("...it stood over the place where the child was.") This information is presented by Matthew for multiple theological reasons, but all revolve around the nativity of Jesus, the Messiah. As Matthew presents them, these two events may be taken as time parameters for Jesus' birth.

An entirely separate stream of tradition, Revelation, describes *a sign in heaven that appeared in the sky, but within those astronomically datable time parameters from Matthew.* John's image in the Revelation is clearly about the birth of Jesus as well. Its details of sun and moon, (and possibly also stars) limit the actual appearance of such an image in the sky to a time within Matthew's parameters. Thus, the birth of Jesus lies within a range of time multiply attested by Matthew and John.

The significance of the Woman clothed with the sun, in a document many decades later than the birth of Jesus and the actual events in the sky at that time, was not lost on those who first received the Revelation. It was known to them, intelligible to them. That is remarkable. We should rid ourselves of any notion that, because we know less about Jesus than we would like to, people of the past must have known even less.

The Woman clothed with the sun in chapter 12 has become the subject of much discussion concerning Jesus' birth, most of it fairly recent. E. L. Martin in *The Star That Astonished the World* maintained that this image tells us exactly when Jesus was born. Many others have also connected the Woman in the vision with Virgo. But there are differences in their assessments of just what this might represent: the time of conception, the time of birth, the time of the birth of the Enochian Son of Man (distant past), or something other than a time reference. We will briefly examine these ideas, but all of them connect the Woman in the vision with the constellation Virgo. Our sky identification is common to the various interpretations.

Remember, this sign was not something anyone could actually have seen with the eye. It happened during the day; stars were not visible. John "saw" it, but in his vision. The moon was a new moon to an observer on earth in September of 3 B.C. Even if the observer could have seen the stars during the day, the moon would not have appeared at all. John in his vision seems to imply that the moon was visible at the Woman's feet. This should remind us that we are in visionary territory primarily.

On the other hand, the circumstances given in the text: standing on the moon and clothed with the sun, occurred at the very time of the Regulus and Jupiter conjunction, which is one of the amazing occurrences in the sky thought by some to be part of a larger series of events that involved the Star of Bethlehem. The cumulative evidence suggests that at least the general time of the conception or birth of Jesus is in mind here.

We in the West know Virgo as the Virgin. This was not a universally held understanding of the constellation. In some cultures the woman of the constellation appeared in the sky with a child. This only matters if the virgin birth of Jesus is being taught or affirmed in the vision. There is no reason to think that it is. Later Christians familiar with Virgo as the virgin may certainly have made that connection, but it is not to be found in the Revelation text itself.

In the Revelation, the Woman bears a male child who is taken to safety with God in heaven. He is to rule the nations with a rod of iron. That is a statement found in Psalm 2. Psalm 2 will be very familiar to Christians. It is a coronation psalm about God's own king. Verse 7 says: "I will tell of the decree: The Lord said to me, 'You are my Son; today I have begotten you.'" The reference to a king ruling with a rod of iron has always been understood by God's people as messianic.

Figure 41. The sky of September 11/12, 3 B.C., as reconstructed by Stellarium. The sun shining in Virgo meant Virgo could not be seen during the day. Astronomers/astrologers knew what was in the sky around the sun by computation, and by observation during heliacal risings of the objects in the sky rising ahead of the sun. The moon was new—completely black, because the sun was shining upon the back side. It should be noted that the sun passes through Virgo each year. A scenario such as this is not rare.

Figure 42. This is the sky of September 11/12 as above, but shown without the effect of the atmosphere. This is an artificial way to present the sky, but it allows us to see that Jupiter and Regulus were in conjunction at just this time within Leo. This conjunction would have been observable before the rising of the sun under normal conditions.

Figure 43. This is another Stellarium image of the sky on September 11/12 3 B.C., but with Arabian sky lore depicted instead of the Western sky lore usually portrayed. The winged woman corresponds to Virgo. The Lion above her head is Leo. The serpent the woman faces in this image corresponds to Hydra. Note the other serpent-like being below her and to the left.

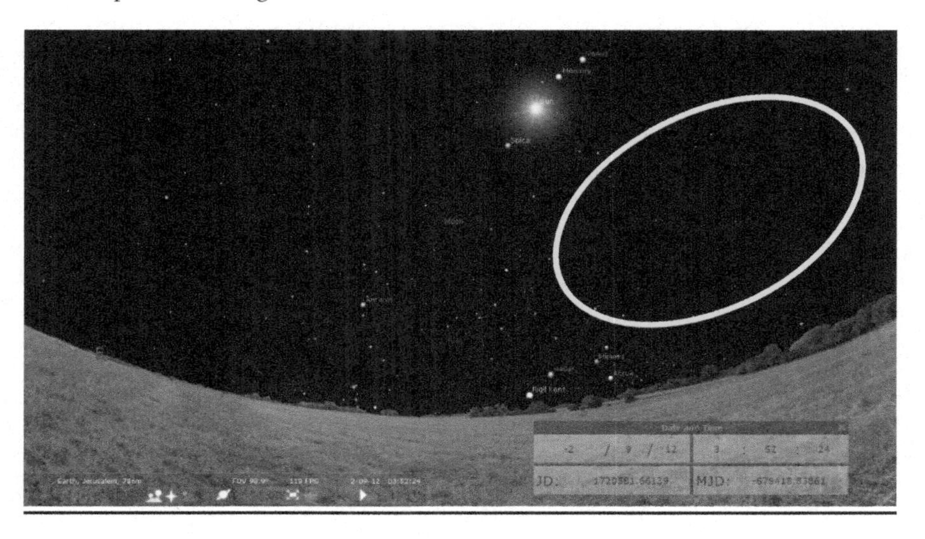

Figure 44. September 11/12 again with the atmosphere eliminated in order to see where the stars would appear if we could see them during the day. The oval inscribed on this illustration shows the region near Hydra's tail. As Malina says, this is an area of the sky with relatively few visible stars. The Dragon's tail swept one third of the stars from the sky in the vision; that further solidifies an identification of Hydra and the Dragon within the vision.

E. L. Martin

In chapter 6 of his book Martin says:

The fact is, however, I can state without a shadow of a doubt, that the celestial scene described by the apostle John in Revelation 12:1–5, if viewed astronomically, would center precisely on a New Moon date within mid-September, and that in 3 B.C.E. that exact celestial phenomenon would have occurred in the early evening of September 11th. I can also state with assurance that sundown on September 11, 3 B.C.E. was also the beginning of the Jewish New Year (Rosh ha-Shanah — The Day of Trumpets). The Star That Astonished the World, page 92

Rick Larson

Rick Larson is an attorney, a Bible investigator, and the producer of *The Star of Bethlehem* documentary. He has followed a good deal of Martin's conclusions and illustrated them well in his video productions. Larson takes the position that the time described when the sun shone in Virgo and the new moon was at her feet should be taken as referring to the conception of Jesus, not his birth. This is interesting, because the Jupiter/Venus conjunction of June 17, 2 B.C., came approximately nine months later. That would then have been the sign of his birth.

But here is a word of caution. The Revelation is not ultimately about any astrologers being right with precision. They were right about the birth of a king in Judea. They were right about approximately when that birth happened. Still, they went first to the wrong place. It may be that the Woman clothed with the sun and standing on the moon preserves a memory of when Jesus was conceived, but the arcane arts of the Magi are not what this is about.

Dag Kihlman

Dag Kihlman, has brought to these discussions the important perspective of astrologers in Mesopotamia. Formerly, the application of astrology has drawn on western lore almost exclusively. Kihlman finds the reference to the Woman's labor pains to be linked to an omen in ancient Mesopotamian lore about difficult deliveries of children. Another omen concerning Jupiter and Regulus, warned of the overthrow and death of the king. Another warned of danger if Jupiter and Venus were together in the sky. The activity of Jupiter before, during, and after that particular time when the Woman in the sky was clothed with the sun, standing on the moon, and having a crown of twelve stars (September 11, 3 B.C.) meant the portent of the Woman was itself significant.

Bruce Malina

Bruce Malina understood this sign in the heavens to refer to the antediluvian period, the time before the flood. For Malina, this scene within the Revelation is about the distant past. While agreeing that the child born is ultimately the Messiah of Israel, Malina first finds a description here of the Son of Man in Enoch. In that book, Enoch is shown a vision of what will happen in the world when God sends a Son of Man to bring in righteousness and end evil. Enoch later learns that he himself is that Son of Man. Of course, this is at odds with the Christian belief that Jesus is the Son of Man as described in Daniel 7.

This should cause us to return to the question: just who is the Woman, and who is the child to be born? Perhaps we need to enlarge our thinking. Is this only one woman in history, Mary? Or is this Woman the chosen people of God from whom the Messiah will come? Is she Sarah? Is she all the faithful women of the past as well as the individual mother of Jesus? If we assume that the purpose of the sign of the Woman clothed with the sun is to tell us *when* Jesus was born—even if it does—we can overlook other meaning within the sign.

Bruce Metzger

Professor Metzger helped many Bible students gain a greater comprehension of the Revelation with his *Breaking the Code (Breaking the Code: Understanding the Book of Revelation.* Nashville: Abingdon. 1993.) Metzger provides a commentary that many will recognize as mainstream. He understands the audience of Revelation to be the persecuted Christians in the time of Emperor Domitian, from AD 81-96. The child is Christ. The Woman is "...probably intended as a personification of the ideal community of God's people, first in its Jewish form in which it was persecuted by a political power as evil as the dragon (12:6)" (p. 74). The Dragon: "...John himself tells us in verse 9 that the dragon represents Satan, the devil." (p. 73).

Colin Nicholl

Colin Nicholl insists that the Star of Bethlehem could only have been a comet, and that the comet first appeared and increased in size within Virgo (Nicholl, Colin R. *The Great Christ Comet: Revealing the True Star of Bethlehem.* Wheaton, Illinois: Crossway, 2015. Pp. 151-176). There are many things to be said in favor of this book. It is extremely well-researched and illustrated. But we find two major difficulties. Nicholl rejects a 1 B.C. death year for Herod, holding the conventional year 4 B.C. as the correct year. In doing so he does find a brief time when the sun was in Virgo, with the moon at the feet of the image. This was in September of 6 B.C. *At just that time* a coma (nucleus of a comet) is supposed to have appeared—not just anywhere in the sky—within Virgo, giving the appearance of a baby growing and about to be born. No sources confirm a coma/comet in that part of the sky at that time. Then, the coma took on the appearance of the scepter in Numbers 24 mentioned parallel to the star in Balaam's oracle. The coma/comet became that which the Magi followed, and indicated the actual house where Jesus was to be found in Bethlehem, due to its configuration in the sky, making it a kind of precise pointer. The appearance of a comet at precisely the right time and place is simply too convenient. Further, no one in Israel seems to have been aware of the extraordinary comet, judging from Matthew 2. In view of its symbolic meaning and its impressive size, the hypothetical comet could hardly have gone unnoticed.

As far as the meaning of the Woman is concerned in John's vision, Nicholl says: "The constellation figure is playing the part of Israel/Mary pregnant, in labor, and delivering her son, the Messiah. John may be deliberately recalling the portrayal of Israel as the Messiah's mother in Micah 5:2-3, the text to which the Jewish scholars turned in order to identify the location of the Messiah's birth for Herod the Great (Matt. 2:5-6)" (*The Great Christ Comet,* pp. 166, 167).

Rumors and Hopes

The Eastern and Western approaches to astrology have been presented briefly. In the East the stars were watched for the omens they provided, cataloged in the scriptures from the ancient wise men of Mesopotamia. In the West astrology became more a system of making predictions about an individual based on sky conditions at birth. There was certainly dialogue between practitioners of the two approaches by the time Jesus was born. Berossus began that dialogue three centuries before Jesus was born.

In all the world, people were waiting. We have reasons to believe that many people in the world before Jesus' birth were expecting the advent of a world leader who would bring a better life for them all. What follows is a series of examples.

Here is a short quotation from the Fourth Eclogue of the Roman poet Virgil.

> Dear child of gods, great progeny of Jove!
> See how it totters- the world's orbed might,
> Earth, and wide ocean, and the vault profound,
> All, see, enraptured of the coming time!
> From Virgil's Fourth Eclogue, c. 42 B.C.

The point is not whether the poet Virgil was actually a non-Israelite prophet who foresaw the birth of Christ, as Constantine and other Christians would later think. The point is not even what Virgil himself meant by his words (Augustus Caesar?). The point is that some people in Virgil's world expected a world-transforming individual to be born and rule. Virgil's poem is either a reflection of such an already-existing belief, or a contributor to its popularity later.

Many Jews remained in Babylon following the nation's exile there in the 6th Century B.C. The Book of Daniel tells us Daniel had been the chief of all wise men there. To the extent that Daniel was remembered, admired, and studied by Jews in Babylon, the coming of a Son of Man was squarely in the minds of the faithful.

Balaam was a seer from the distant past. The Balaam inscription found in 1967 at Tell Deir Alla in Jordan provides evidence that this man was remembered for centuries because of his supposed paranormal abilities. In the Book of Numbers, Balaam is summoned by the local Amalekite King Balak to place a curse on the nation of Israel. Balaam fails to do so in the end, and blesses Israel instead three times. Balaam knows better than to offend God this way. Balaam delivers four oracles in Numbers. His fourth is in chapter 24:

> [15] *And he took up his discourse and said,*
> *"The oracle of Balaam the son of Beor,*
> *the oracle of the man whose eye is opened,*
> [16] *the oracle of him who hears the words of God,*
> *and knows the knowledge of the Most High,*
> *who sees the vision of the Almighty,*
> *falling down with his eyes uncovered:*
> [17] *I see him, but not now;*
> *I behold him, but not near:*
> *a star shall come out of Jacob,*
> *and a scepter shall rise out of Israel;*
> *it shall crush the forehead of Moab*
> *and break down all the sons of Sheth.*
> [18] *Edom shall be dispossessed;*

Seir also, his enemies, shall be dispossessed.
Israel is doing valiantly.
[19] *And one from Jacob shall exercise dominion*
and destroy the survivors of cities!"
Numbers 24:17-19

Centuries later at Qumran this oracle was very much remembered as a prophecy of a coming Messiah in a document among the Dead Sea Scrolls called the Testimonia (4Q175).

Tacitus, the Roman historian, wrote the following about the fall of Jerusalem in 70 AD. "Some few put a fearful meaning on these events, but in most there was a firm persuasion, that in the ancient records of their priests was contained *a prediction of how at this very time the East was to grow powerful, and rulers, coming from Judaea, were to acquire universal empire."* In this Tacitus echoes Josephus. (Tacitus Histories 5:13.)

Zoroastrian influence in the East stressed the coming of a messianic figure at some time in the future. This belief was far-reaching and constant in Mesopotamia. The figure was known as the Saoshyant, Bringer of Benefit. We have briefly mentioned him. He would radically change the world, waging war against demonic forces, bringing justice, ending suffering, serving Ahuru Mazda, the Light God. Since Magi comprised a priestly caste within the Zoroastrian religion, this expectation is extremely relevant to our investigation.

Stellar Individuals

Some events in the sky were exceedingly rare and spectacular. When these took place astrologers must have reasoned differently from their normal patterns. That is, they did not simply conclude that hundreds or thousands of people in general who were being born at the time of the extraordinary event would be extraordinarily influenced. They reasoned that because of the unique nature of that unique sky event, a truly unique *individual* was being born or dying somewhere. Greatness of this kind is not shared with the multitudes, but with rare individuals.

We have evidence that ancient people associated unique sky events like eclipses and comets with births and deaths of individual, world-changing people in history:

- Alexander the Great Several legends were told about Alexander's birth, one involving the sky. His mother Olympias dreamed that a lightning bolt struck her womb. Lightning may not seem to us like something from the realm of the stars and planets, but that is because we have knowledge of the atmosphere and of space.
- Julius Caesar After Julius Caesar died in 44 B.C., a comet appeared in the sky for seven days. His nephew Octavian claimed this was a sign of Julius Caesar's deification. This helped Octavian become the accepted successor, Augustus Caesar, and marked the end of the Republic in favor of the Empire.
- Cleopatra Dio Cassius said the death of Cleopatra in 30 B.C. was followed by the appearance of comets. This may be a reference to a yearly meteor shower.
- Augustus Caesar Before his death, according to Cassius Dio, "the sun suffered a total eclipse and most of the sky seemed to be on fire; glowing embers appeared to be falling from it and blood-red comets were seen," (Cassius Dio Book 56 Chapter 29)
- Mithridates VI Eupator He was the King of the Hellenistic Kingdom of Pontus from 135 to 63 B.C. A successful king, he kept the Roman Republic at bay. Legend said that a comet accompanied his birth to indicate that he would be a great, messianic type of ruler. He was a descendent of Alexander the Great, making the omen more believable.

Interpreting it all…

Interpreting the sky was not an exact science, to be sure. Josephus is basically right that astrology came from Babylonia to Greece, and then to Rome. It did not remain unchanged in the West. It becomes impossible to say that Magi from the East would never employ ideas found in the West. We simply don't know that, and it goes against reason to think so, given the time that passed between Berossus and the birth of Jesus.

But the basic framework of the sky was essentially the same for East and West: zodiacal signs, planets moving through them, sun and moon constantly in motion.

The mapping of the world is similar between the Eastern and Western astrological systems as well. The earth is in each case divided into four main regions, and sky phenomenon relate to particular places. Koch-Westenholz says of traditional Babylonian astrology: "…it is geographically oriented —many of its apodoses apply to specific countries, cities or nations," (p. 19). This is very important to us in our investigation, because one of the questions we must answer is: Why did the Magi decide that the king they were looking for would be found in Herod's realm? In what way did the sky point them there?

The thought that the Magi were riding their camels by night and sleeping by day so they could follow the star is not at all supported by the biblical text, or by even an introductory knowledge of astrology. The Magi went to Jerusalem, because they had already read the sky, and Jerusalem was where they believed the sky had directed them. It was a capital city.

In the West

The astrologer Claudius Ptolemy (c. 100-170 A.D.) in his *Tetrabiblos*, expressing Western astrological thought, sees the world in four quadrants and lists the countries that fall under the influence of each of the twelve zodiacal signs. But some of the countries in the "second quadrant" are near the middle of the earth, so their situation is affected by the "northwest triplicity" These countries are: "Idumaea, Coelesyria, **Judaea,** Phoenicia, Chaldaea, Orchynia, and Arabia Felix" (Claudius Ptolemy, Tetrabiblos. Tr J.M. Ashmand. Pacific Publishing Studio, p. 41). "...they have for their rulers, Jupiter and Mars, together with Mercury." (p. 41) So, an astrologer looking for the significance of spectacular sky events involving Jupiter, Mars, and/or Mercury might look to Judea as one place where their influence would be seen on earth. These three planets, Jupiter especially, would present the kind of signs astrologers looked for at the general time of Jesus' birth.

In the East

Remember, Koch-Westenholz says this of the Eastern system: "In astrology, an omen was often seen to pertain to one of the four geographical entities Akkad (South), Subartu (North), Elam (East) and Amurru (West)." (p. 98). But ultimately all astrology was a matter of interpretation. Surely there were many times when one eastern astrologer reached one particular conclusion when other astrologers thought the opposite was true. "The unusual wealth of reports illustrates well the wildly conflicting approaches possible in interpreting the same celestial phenomena," (Koch-Westenholz, p. 145.)

"The individual astrologer's judgement of what seems relevant plays a decisive role in what omina are selected. It is immediately obvious that this thought pattern has analogies elsewhere. The closest parallel is that of a rabbi acting as a judge in a legal dispute. He would search through the traditional texts for a parallel to the case in question, and apply the recorded verdict to the present case. Talmudic law is suggestive, not normative, to the extent that 'he who believes that the ox in the Talmud is a real ox has not even begun to understand *halakha* (tradition)'. Rules given for a goring ox may be applied to a biting dog, or to any other case that appears similar; Biblical injunctions against kindling or extinguishing fire on the Sabbath have been applied in modern times to turning on or off electrical appliances." (Koch-Westenholz, p. 150.)

In the case of Mesopotamian astrology and its omens lists, we have specific words concerning Amurru, the area including Herod's Judea. Again, Kihlman contends that what the Magi saw in the heavens was not a joyful sight for them, but a threatening one. Jupiter had indeed passed Regulus, and retrograded back out of Leo. The Empire was in danger unless someone asked for peace. This rare astrological event took place within the very time frame we are examining for the birth of Christ.

The Star Reappears

After its breathtaking conjunction with Venus on June 17, 2 B.C., Jupiter moved further westward each night until it disappeared below the horizon. After nine months it re-emerged in heliacal rise ahead of the sun. That was in late 2 B.C. This comports with Matthew 2:9-10 which implies that the star came back into view after a period of absence. Jupiter was again approaching its station where it would stop in the sky with reference to the field of fixed stars.

Heliacal risings were of great interest to astrologers, East or West. We should have no doubt that they observed the sky early in the morning, before dawn. Matthew's Magi who had not found the King they were looking for in Jerusalem, leading city of Amurru, the enemy, were now directed by the Jewish Scripture experts in the capital city to Bethlehem.

> *"But you, O Bethlehem Ephrathah,*
> *who are too little to be among the clans of Judah,*
> *from you shall come forth for me*
> *one who is to be ruler in Israel,*
> *whose coming forth is from of old,*
> *from ancient days."* Micah 5:2

When they looked at the pre-dawn sky from their Jerusalem location, they saw exactly what the Gospel of Matthew reports. Jupiter was shining at sixty-two degrees above the horizon in a direction South South-west. That was in the exact direction they were already planning to travel, the direction toward Bethlehem, five miles away. At this particular place in the sky, and only at this particular time, Jupiter appeared to be directly over the town. It was now in its station, i.e, stopped in the sky with reference to the fixed stars.

The succession of Jupiter events lasted 16 months from its first appearance in heliacal rise with Venus. “We have seen his star at its rising” identifies the Star as either Venus or Jupiter. Venus was associated with Jupiter at times during this period as we have seen. In Revelation Jesus is “the bright morning star”, which is a reference to Venus. But Venus did not enter its station above Bethlehem as Jupiter did. We may identify the Star of Bethlehem as Jupiter, the kings’ planet. In combination with Venus, with Regulus, and other planets also, it was Jupiter that Matthew’s Magi interpreted as the sign of the birth of the King of the Jews.

Herod ordered the killing of all boys in or near Bethlehem up to the age of two years, based on the time of the star’s appearance which he had obtained from the Magi. This, too, is consistent with Jupiter as the Star, because sixteen months rounded upward to the next full year is two years.

Figure 45. This is what the Magi would have seen in their early morning observation of the sky at Jerusalem, Jupiter above Bethlehem. Jupiter had come to its station, its stopping point against the stars. This is exactly what the Gospel of Matthew describes. Jupiter is the bright object high and to the right of center in this illustration. Stellarium.

In the conjunctions of Jupiter and Venus the Magi must have found meaning not limited to their own country. The heliacal rise of Jupiter with Venus must have already suggested the birth of some extraordinary person. The second conjunction, during which the planets seemed to fuse in the sky, happened to the West, directly over the western horizon. In fact, it was only fifteen degrees north of a true compass heading from Ctesiphon to Jerusalem. Eastern astrology would indicate that it was time to make peace with Amurru in the West. Western astrology held Jupiter to be the ruler of certain regions toward the middle of the earth, including Judaea. Either school of astrology might have caused the Magi to travel to the West, some six hundred miles from Ctesiphon. Between these conjunctions the sun moved into Virgo and the moon was briefly at her feet. This was nine months before the June 17 conjunction. If only in retrospect, the Magi may have been the first to notice this and interpret it as a sign of the conception of a king in Amurru.

There were several good reasons for people who studied the stars to find more meaning in these events than just the disaster to befall the Parthian King. People of the world shared an expectation of a coming king unlike all others. It was true in Judea, and it was true in Parthia. If that person were to be born, what greater sights in the heavens could attend his birth than the sights of 2 B.C.? Magi must have all have hoped someday to be able to announce the coming of such a king. The sky gave them reason to believe that the time had come.

Aries was the constellation associated with Israel. Leo was not. Some have made a connection between the Lion in the sky and the Lion of the tribe of Judah, but that would probably not have entered the minds of ancient Magi. This would only have been true if the Magi were greatly influenced by Jews, or were Jews themselves. That is not impossible, but unlikely.

Clement of Alexandria wrote in the Second Century that the Magi had come from Parthia (Stromata 1:15). The Church of the Nativity in Bethlehem was spared destruction by Persian invaders in 614 because of a painting above the door showing the Magi dressed in Parthian clothing. Such was the belief about their origin already long ago. We have seen evidence strongly suggesting that Parthia was the Magis' home, though other locations remain possible. The preponderance of evidence suggests that Parthian ambassadors from the Megistanes crossed the wilderness to bring gifts to a King of Amurru who had recently been born, and thereby to attempt to secure peace with this kingdom, as their star lore directed them to do.

Whoever the Magi were and wherever they came from, they surely traveled in larger numbers than three for the sake of security. Among their party must have been guards for their gold, frankincense, and myrrh, as well as for themselves. If they in fact represented the government of the Empire of Parthia as it seems, they no doubt came with soldiers known as Parthian Cataphracts. They would have come in numbers not large enough to be taken as a threat, but large enough to protect the members of the House of the Magi and their possessions. One hundred or more of such soldiers would not have been unreasonable.

Josephus records that treasure caravans brought expensive offerings to Jerusalem from Jews living in Parthian territory with "many ten thousand men" (Antiquities 18:9:1). Plutarch (Crassus, p. 21) writes of Surenas, a Parthian military commander and possibly a member of the Megistanes, who traveled with a caravan of cavalry, servants, and attendants of great size: "a baggage train of 1,000 camels".

It is actually possible that the Magis' company outnumbered the residents of Bethlehem at that time. When they arrived they inquired about male children who had been born there in recent days. The presence of Joseph, Mary, and Jesus was no secret in Bethlehem.

> *"When they saw the star, they rejoiced exceedingly with great joy. And going into the house, they saw the child with Mary his mother, and they fell down and worshiped him. Then, opening their treasures, they offered him gifts, gold and frankincense and myrrh."* Matthew 2:10-11

Kihlman provides an important insight into verse 10. The star lore of the ancient Mesopotamians said: "If Jupiter becomes steady in the morning, enemy kings will be reconciled." (Reiner and Pingree [1998], p. 244; Kihlman p. 99). This is exactly what the Magi observed over Bethlehem with Jupiter in its station before dawn. It would have indicated that their mission to secure peace had been successful. Therefore, they rejoiced. Then, warned in a dream, they went back to their homeland without meeting Herod again. When Herod learned that the company of Magi and guards had suddenly left Bethlehem, the anger he had become known for led to his barbarous order concerning the children of the Bethlehem area.

It is clear that in Matthew's text *the experiences and language of astrological specialists have come down to us through the memories and reports of non-specialists.* The non-astrologers related what they learned from the Magi in their own ways. So, "We have seen his star in its heliacal rise," became "We have seen his star at its rising." The station of Jupiter in the predawn of December 25 became "…it stood over the place where the child was." The Magi's sense of joy that their peace mission had succeeded, because Jupiter was in its station at dawn became… "When they saw the star, they rejoiced exceedingly with great joy (2:10)." This contributes to the credibility of the story.

Other parts of the story have been so engrained in the public's view that we need to stop and carefully realize what Matthew does and does not say. First, nowhere does he say there were three Magi. The "going before them" of the star with respect to the Magi has become interpreted as though the star were traveling ahead of the Magi to lead them. Matthew's text cannot be pressed to mean that. *Proagein* may only mean here that the star was in the direction they were going. The "standing of the star above the place where the child was" is often thought of as marking the individual house where Joseph, Mary, and Jesus were. Again, Matthew's text cannot be pressed to mean only that. It has been assumed by readers because of deeply entrenched, later traditions.

The possible sources for the information in Matthew 2 include: (1) members of Jesus' own family, (2) residents of

Bethlehem even years later, (3) members of the Jerusalem Aristocracy who later became followers of Jesus themselves. Think of Nicodemus or Joseph of Arimathea, for example. People such as this would have been the kind of Scripture experts summoned by Herod, who said the Messiah would come from Bethlehem. They were not ignorant of the events of earlier days and years.

What Does This Mean?

First this means the story in Matthew 2 is a true story, despite assertions to the contrary. The reported phenomena concerning the star have their counterparts in the events that happened on the earth and in the sky in 3 and 2 B.C. Questions have been addressed. Objections have been answered. The integrity of the Scriptures has been upheld. Faith in the God who has given us the Scriptures has been affirmed. The story makes perfect sense in the context of its time and place. It is not an invention, but a retelling in ordinary terms of an extraordinary set of events that involved the sky, and people who studied it.

Second, it means prophesies have been fulfilled. We have encountered the Micah prophecy about Bethlehem (Micah 5:2), and the Balaam oracle about the rising star from Jacob (Numbers 24:15-19). We must understand that these are more than just predictions. These prophetic passages deal with the larger theme of the coming of the Messiah.

"A voice was heard in Ramah, weeping and loud lamentation, Rachel weeping for her children; she refused to be comforted, because they are no more" (Matthew 2:18). This quotation of Jeremiah 31:15 is also more than simply a prediction; it invokes the matriarch Rachel whose grave is at Bethlehem. Though Rachel had been gone from the earth for many centuries, the children murdered by Herod were her children also. This act of killing them was a crime against the whole people of Israel. But surrounding these words in Jeremiah are words of encouragement from God that weeping will end because of what the Lord will do for his people. All of this had now begun to be fulfilled.

A further prophetic passage is indirectly to be found in Matthew 2. "*A multitude of camels shall cover you, the young camels of Midian and Ephah; all those from Sheba shall come. They shall bring gold and frankincense, and shall bring good news, the praises of the* L*ORD.*" Isaiah 60:6

The visit of the Magi speaks to that future time when God's people will be restored and blessed. The Magi's gifts of gold and frankincense brings this Isaiah passage to mind. Signs of that future God has promised have already been glimpsed now in the gold and frankincense, and in the Star. The other nations of the world, represented by the Magi, will come to the Messiah, Jesus. This will be true even if God's chosen people resist. God's great work of redeeming the world is under way.

Some have seen in this story a condemnation of the practice of magic found in the pagan world. There does not seem to be any evidence for that within Matthew's text, although it would be consistent with the Old Testament and the New. R. E. Brown (*The Birth of the Messiah*, p. 168) has it right: "They (the Magi) represent the best of pagan lore and religious perceptivity which has come to seek Jesus through revelation in nature." They required the Scriptures in order to find the King they were looking for; their astrology was not enough. Their methods only brought them close. What they expected to find was surely a prince in a palace. They discovered instead a child from a poor family living in a small village. But they were looking, in contrast to religious leaders, five miles from Bethlehem, who were not. While looking for him who was actually the Light of the World, and with the help of the prophet Micah, they managed to find him.

Years later a Gentile Centurion would send a request to Jesus to simply give the word so that his servant would be healed at a distance (Luke 7:6). Jesus was amazed at his faith. Already during Jesus' public ministry there were Gentiles whose faith put them ahead of God's schedule. Not until Pentecost, following Jesus' death, resurrection, and ascension, did the church in the power of the Holy Spirit begin to take the Gospel to all the nations of the world.

In their own way, the Magi are among those perceptive Gentiles. The good news of the Gospel of Jesus Christ was already breaking out in the world, long before its scheduled arrival. In thirty-three years Jesus' Gospel would begin to sweep through the world in an effort led by Peter, Paul, and all the rest of Jesus' Apostles. But for these seekers from the East, his revelation was already under way.

As a star God's Holy Word
Leads us to our King and Lord;
Brightly from its sacred pages
Shall this light throughout the ages
Shine upon our path of life,
Shine upon our path of life.

"Bright and Glorious is the Sky"
Verse 6, Nikolai F. S. Grundtvig

Partial Summary of Sky Events in 3 and 2 B.C.

DATE: May 3 B.C. Mars retrogrades in Capricorn.

DATE: August 12, 3 B.C.

EVENT: Jupiter and Venus in close heliacal rise.

ASTROLOGICAL SIGNIFICANCE: "In all cases when the distances between planets or luminaries are but trifling, the planet which precedes is said to apply to that which follows; and that which follows to be separating from the one which precedes." Ptolomy, Tetrabiblos, p. 33. (Does this mean Venus would apply its positive influences to Jupiter's already positive influence?)

"The greatest good fortune and great fame—consular or proconsular power—result from Jupiter in the eleventh house...that is, if she is on such a course as was described in connection with the fifth house." Firmicus Maternus, Ancient Astrology, p. 82. (The fifth house is Leo where Jupiter appeared.)

Heliacal rise implies birth(s) affected.

"If Venus enters Jupiter (UD.AL.Tar): the king of Akkad will die, the dynasty will change, either a soldier will go out or the enemy will send a message (asking for peace) to the land." Reiner, Erica and David Pingree. Babylonian Planetary Omens Part Three, p.93.

POLITICAL CIRCUMSTANCES: In Rome, Augustus Caesar prepares for the 750th anniversary of the founding of the city, as well as his 25th anniversary as Emperor. Oaths of allegiance are collected from across the empire; Augustus will be named Father of the Country.

Sometime in late 3 B.C. or early 2 B.C., Queen Musa of Parthia and her son poison the King. They seize the throne as Phraates V and Queen Musa. Armenia is part of the Roman Empire, but it is located near the western border of the Parthian Empire. Peace prevails for now. Phraates V enters Armenia.

DATE: August 24/25 3 B.C. Venus and Mercury conjunct - tion inLeo.

DATE: September 10/11 3 B.C.

EVENT: "Woman clothed with the sun" (Revelation 12). The sun shines at the center of Virgo, and the new moon is beneath her feet.The twelve stars are either the 12 visible stars near Virgo's head, or the bright stars near Virgo's head plus the planets Jupiter, Venus, and Mercury.

ASTROLOGICAL SIGNIFICANCE: Kihlman looks at the Mesopotamian omens lists and concludes that this would have been seen as a harbinger of difficult childbirth. (Star, p. 113.)

HISTORICAL CIRCUMSTANCES: Some believe this provides the exact time when Jesus was born—when Virgo was in this configuration with sun, moon, and stars.

DATE: September 10, 3B.C. As the Moon moves past the Sun to become waxing, the star Regulus meets nearly all the conditions shown below. In addition, Jupiter is beginning a triple conjunction with Regulus.

ASTROLOGICAL SIGNIFICANCE: "The fifth degree of Leo has a splendidly glowing star. If the waxing moon is found in this star, if it is exactly on the ascendant or on the MC, this indicates the highest royal and imperial power." Maternus, Astrology, p. 183.

DATE: September 14, 3 B.C.

EVENT: First of three Jupiter Regulus conjunctions in Leo. Jupiter reaches its station on November 25 and begins to retrograde.

POLITICAL CIRCUMSTANCES: In 2 B.C. Phraates IV moves into Armenia, which belongs to Rome. This risks war between the two empires, Rome and Parthia.

DATE: February 17, 2 B.C.

EVENT: Second of three Jupiter Regulus conjunctions in Leo. Jupiter reaches its station March 28/29 after retrograding out of the breast of Leo. Then it resumes its normal motion against the fixed stars.

ASTROLOGICAL SIGNIFICANCE: "And the matter of the planet Jupiter is as follows: If it turns back out of the Breast of Leo, this is ominous. It is written in the Series as follows: 'If Jupiter passes Regulus and gets ahead of it, and afterwards Regulus, which it passed and got ahead of, stays within in its setting, someone will rise, kill the king, and seize the throne.'" (Letters from Assyrian and Babylonian Scholars)

POLITICAL CIRCUMSTANCES: The Parthian Magi House within the Megistanes is likely concerned that the new king, Phraates V, will be killed next, just as he recently killed his own father, as foretold by Jupiter and Venus in heliacal rise during the past year. His actions in Armenia are provoking war with the Roman Empire.

DATE: May 8, 2 B.C.

EVENT: Third of three Jupiter Regulus conjunctions in Leo.

ASTROLOGICAL SIGNIFICANCE: The activity of Jupiter and Regulus is ominous for Parthia according to the ancient omens, but conversely a sign of good fortune for Amurru, the West. Jupiter is the common "star" in all that has transpired. Magi must reason that Jupiter, the "king's star", is the natal star of the king in the West.

POLITICAL CIRCUMSTANCES: Magi consider a diplomatic mission to the West in order to secure peace, rather than suffer a disastrous war. Their classic omens have warned them that they should seek peace.They do not plan to go to Rome, but to the king their star lore has directed them to find.

DATE: June 17, 2 B.C.

EVENT: Jupiter Venus conjunction over the western horizon at nightfall. The planets were separated by only one half archminute (an archminute is equal to 1 60th of one degree). To the eye they appeared to have merged. This amazing conjunction was unparalleled in ancient history. Jupiter and Venus are the brightest objects in the night sky after the moon. Such conjunctions are both remarkable sights, and extremely rare ones-centuries apart. No living magus had seen such a conjunction before.

ASTROLOGICAL SIGNIFICANCE: Clearly, this meant to eastern astrologers like the Magi that a figure of international importance had been born. The conjunction appeared in the West, confirming earlier omens about Amurru.

POLITICAL CIRCUMSTANCES: If they had not already set out on a journey to the West, after this astonishing conjunction, the Magi from the Parthian government left to secure peace with Amurru. Informed by eastern and western sky lore, and by popular and religious beliefs that a world ruler would come from Israel, Herod's kingdom, and its capital, Jerusalem, was their first destination.

DATE: August 29, 2 B.C.

EVENT: Jupiter, Mars, Mercury, Venus, sun and moon in Virgo. "Woman clothed with the sun" again.

ASTROLOGICAL SIGNIFICANCE: "For example, should the two luminaries be found in masculine signs...they being at the same time especially attended by a doryphory composed of all five planets...the persons then about to be born will become kings or princes...attendant stars themselves be in angles...the said persons will become great, powerful, and mighty in the world." (Ptolomy, Tetrabiblos, p. 105) This is Ptolomy's example. In fact, on August 29, only Saturn was missing. Both sun and moon were present in the doryphory. "If Jupiter comes into aspect with the waxing Moon, thiswill create men of almost divine and immortal nature." Firmicus Maternus, Ancient Astrology, p. 80.

DATE: December 25, 2 B.C.

EVENT: Jupiter has reappeared in the East after being gone from sight for months. On this day it is in station again, stopped against the fixed stars. In the early morning before sunrise, the time of observation of heliacal rise, Jupiter is high over the horizon, south south-west.

ASTROLOGICAL SIGNIFICANCE: The locations of stars were important to astrologers. From their vantage point in Jerusalem, the Magi saw Jupiter stopped (in station) above Bethlehem. This was a further indication that the king they were looking for would be found there (as the Jewish Scripture scholars in Jerusalem had told them). They rejoiced when they saw Jupiter again in station. Kihlman points out that this was an omen for eastern Magi that their peace mission would be successful. Star. p. 99.

POLITICAL CIRCUMSTANCES: Herod sends the Magi to Bethlehem. They find the child, but leave for home by another way. Herod orders the killing of all male children in and around Bethlehem up to two years of age, based on the time the star had first appeared.

Selected Works

Brown, R. E. *The Birth of the Messiah, New Updated Edition.* TheAnchor Yale Bible. (New Haven, Connecticut: Yale University Press, 1993).

Enoch. *The Book of Enoch,* tr. R. H. Charles. (Overland Park,Kansa: Digireads.com Publishing, 2018).

Ferrari d'Occhieppo, Konradin. *Der Stern von Bethlehem in astronomischer Sicht. Legende oder Tatsache?* (Giessen: Brunnen-Verlag, 1999).

Finegan, Jack. *Handbook of Biblical Chronology: Principles of Time Reckoning in the Ancient World and Problems of Chronologyin the Bible, Revised Edition* (Peabody, Massachusetts: Hendrickson Publishers, 1998).

Flammarion, C. & Guillemin, E. "Le Cadran Solaire a Retrogradation de l'Observatoire de Juvisy, et le Miracle d'Isaie".L'Astronomie, vol. 4, pp.321-340, September 1885. code 1885LAstr...4..321F.

Henriksson, Göran. *"Aristotle, King David, King Zhou and Pharaoh Thutmosis III Have Seen Comet Encke.".* Mediterranean Archaeology and Archaeometry Vol. 20, No 1, (2020), pp. 29-43 Open Access. Online & Print

Jacobsen, Thorkild. *The Treasures of Darkness: A History of Mesopotamian Religion*, Yale University Press, 1976.

Können, Gunther P., Glenn Schneider, Evan H. Zucker, and PanuLahtinen. Subsuns and Rainbows During Solar Eclipses. AppliedOptics vol. 59, number 21, 20 July, 2020.

Kihlman, Dag. *The Star of Bethlehem and Babylonian Astrology.* (Trollhätten, Sweden: Dag Kihlman, 2018). Larson, Frederick. *The Star of Bethlehem* DVD.

Malina, Bruce. *On the Genre and Message of Revelation.* Hendrickson Publishers, 1995.

Brian G. Marsden and Zdenek Sekanina, "Comets and Nongravitational Forces, VI. Periodic Comet Encke 1786-1971". Astronomical Journal 79 (1974).

Martin, Ernest L. *The Star That Astonished the World.* (Portland,Oregon: Academy for Scriptural Knowledge, 1991).

Maternus, Firmicus. *Ancient Astrology Theory and Practice* (*Matheseos Libri VIII, Astrology Classics,* tr. Jean Rhys Bram. BelAir, MD: The Astrology Center of America, 1975).

Metzger, Bruce. *Breaking the Code: Understanding the Book ofRevelation.* Abingdon, 1993.

NASA. Five Millennia of Solar Eclipses. https://eclipse.gsfc.nasa.gov/SEcat5/catalog.html

Nicholl, Colin R. *The Great Christ Comet: Revealing the True Starof Bethlehem.* (Wheaton, Illinois: Crossway, 2015.)

Parpola, Simo. *Letters from Assyrian and Babylonian Scholars,* SAA 10 (Helsinki: Helsinki University Press, 1993).

Preskar, Peter. "The Assyrians — The Appalling Lords of Torture: Impalement, flaying, and amputations were the trademark of the Assyrians," Dec 27, 2020. Lessons from History https://medium.com/lessons-from-history/assyrians-torture-60fabb7a9642.

Ptolemy, Claudius. *Ptolemy's Tetrabiblos* (tr. J. M. Ashmand.Seattle: Pacific Publishing Studio, 2011).

Reiner, Erica and David Pingree. *Babylonian Planetary OmensPart Three,* Cuneiform Monographs 11 (Groningen, Styx Publications, 1998).

Rochberg, Francesca. *In the Path of the Moon, Babylonian Celestial Divination and Its Legacy,* Studies in Ancient Magic andDivination, vol. 6. (Leiden: Brill, 2010).

Rosenberg, Roy A. "The 'Star of the Messiah' Reconsidered." *Biblica*, vol. 53, no. 1, 1972, pp. 105–109. *JSTOR*,www.jstor.org/stable/42609680. Accessed 31 Jan. 2021.

Sherwin-White, A. N. *Roman Law and Roman Society in the NewTestament* (Oxford: Oxford University Press, 1963, reprinted by Baker Book House, Grand Rapids, Michigan, 1978, 1992).

Vardaman, Jerry, Edwin M. Yamauchi, eds. *Chronos, Kairos, Christos: Nativity and Chronological Studies Presented to Jack Finegan.* (University Park, Pennsylvania: Eisenbrauns, 1989).

Y. Yadin. "The Dial of Ahaz"." *Eretz-Israel: Archaeological, Historical and Geographical Studies* (1958): 91-96. Accessed May 6, 2021. http://www.jstor.org/stable/23612438.

ABOUT THE AUTHOR

Frederick Baltz earned his B.A. from Dana College, 1974.; M.Div. from Wartburg Theological Seminary, 1978; S.T.M. from Wartburg Theological Seminary, 1980. D.Min. University of Dubuque Theological Seminary, 1992. Dr. Baltz has taught for the Institute of Lutheran Theology, Brookings, South Dakota, and has served as its Interim President. He is the author of curriculum, numerous articles and books. Among his books are *Herod* (2006); *Views of Baptism* (2009); *The Mystery of the Beloved Disciple* (2010), and *The Lord Our Healer* (2014). More recently he has written *Exodus Found* (2020) dealing with the Exodus from Egypt, locating it in time with astronomy, and in place, making the case for Timna, Israel, as the crossing point of the "Red Sea." Dr. Baltz has special interest in those areas where biblical studies intersect with the sky. He is Pastor Emeritus of St. Matthew Lutheran Church in Galena, Illinois. He resides there with Cindy; they have four children and seven grandchildren.

Made in the USA
Coppell, TX
18 April 2022